Lean Construction

One Company's Journey to Success

Ted J. Angelo

ANGELO LEAN
CONSTRUCTION

Lean Construction: One Company's Journey to Success by Ted J. Angelo

Printed in the United States of America

Text & Cover Design by Rogue Wave Designs, LLC.
Edited by Erik Gunn, Carolyn Kott Washburne
Indexed by Sylvia Coates

First Edition: 2012
10 9 8 7 6 5 4 3 2 1

ISBN: 0984961003

Printed and bound:
Thomson-Shore, Inc.
Dexter, MI.
734-426-3939

To the Angelo family,
all four generations.

TABLE OF CONTENTS

Acknowledgements

I would like to acknowledge a number of people who have been helpful to me in this journey.

First, the members of our Lean Steering Committee, who over the years have put up with my passion, which at times may have been a bit overwhelming (to put it mildly)!

Next, my assistant, Rowann Dooley, who has managed so many of the details of our Lean processes, which has enabled me to continually look at the larger picture.

To Larry Rubrich, affectionately referred to as "Lean Larry," who initially helped us begin our journey, and who continually offered support over the years with his practical approach to Lean.

To Jerry Stapleton, your assistance proved invaluable in providing contacts for editorial professionals and in putting the final touches on the manuscript.

To the Business Excellence Consortium for providing the opportunity to visit and observe other companies who were on the Lean journey.

All the team members who have had to listen to me continually talk about always looking for waste and how can we do better.

To Paul Grunau, who shared this vision and provided the financial investment necessary for the success of the implementation of lean processes.

Finally, a special thanks to my family: to my children, Sal and Rose, who, as teenagers, had to sit through many videos on Lean; to my daughter-in-law, Amanda, who patiently listened to all the Lean stories; and to my wife, Priscilla, for the numerous times I tried to apply what I was learning to the Angelo home! Thanks for your support.

FOREWORD

Ted Angelo and I worked together for 20 years. When I first entered the construction business, he was a trusted mentor. Our subsequent partnership leading the Grunau Company for 15 years will always be a cherished professional and personal journey.

When we started in the early 1990s, our company faced a number of challenges. Thanks to the efforts of a great group of people, we made progress and experienced meaningful success. One big obstacle, though, continued to confound us. In the specialty construction business, the largest variable cost is labor: labor to fabricate and install the product—in our case mechanical systems such as heating, air conditioning, plumbing, fire protection, and specialty metals. We made progress in many areas of our business, but we were unable to move the needle with regard to our largest variable cost. I remember, when we would ask each other or our colleagues, hearing, "That is just the way it is," or "It's been that way for as long as I can remember."

How could it be that 30 to 40 percent of our cost of doing business is unchangeable? When we really thought about it, we realized that if we could make meaningful progress on this item, we could create a significant, defendable competitive advantage. But how to do it?

It was clear to us that we had to think about this challenge differently. This was not a construction challenge, it was an *efficiency and productivity* challenge. We needed to look at what the best companies, regardless of industry, were doing to drive efficiency and productivity. We found that those companies that had the most significant success applied the principles of efficiency and productivity through an application of Lean concepts—in the field, in the office, and throughout the entire organization.

What follows in this book is the description of our Lean journey. I am sure that there are lots of other books out there that talk about Lean, so why is this one worth the investment?

First of all, this story is written by a person on the ground, in the middle of the journey. The practical insights that position affords take the book from the theoretical to the real. This is a real story, about real experiences, good and bad. If you want to learn more about Lean principles and processes, about what to expect if you embark on a Lean journey, and gain the value of someone who has walked in those footsteps, you will find value in these pages.

More than that, though, you will find that the Lean journey is really a celebration of intellect, creativity, and teamwork. Every company has a Lean journey inside it waiting to happen. One of my favorite moments in the Lean journey is the Team Report-out, which occurs at the end of a Lean event, when the team members report to the company what they accomplished and why. This is where you see the power of a motivated team that owns the results and whose ideas and efforts are respected by each other and by the company community. If you can consistently unlock that potential in your company, you will have a defendable competitive advantage, and a proud workforce.

The Lean journey is about eliminating waste and creating value for stakeholders. It is also about creating an environment of trust, respect, and ownership. I think it's safe to say we all want that.

— Paul Grunau

1 Journey Begins

As far back as I can remember, I have always had an interest in organization. As a teenager, I loved baseball. To make sure I was ready for the next game, I would place a hardball in my glove and put a rubber band around the outside to shape the glove's contour so I could catch hot ground balls in the infield. Designing mechanical systems before the computer (now I am really dating myself), I tried to create a form for just about everything. Early in my construction career, I wanted to improve flow of material when sent to the job. So I used an accountant's pad with multiple columns in order to separate the same type of materials per floor or area. I created a Tool Transfer form for tracking tools to be shipped to the job and returned. One form after another, it just went on and on.

Looking back, I spent 25 years getting ready for "Lean" and didn't even know it.

My first encounter with Lean was not Lean Construction, but Lean Manufacturing. My business reading had given me a passing knowledge of the Toyota Production System and the Lean principles that had already been used in manufacturing for some time. What I read appealed to my sense of organization: Toyota has worked toward perfecting their system over the years by establishing certain ways of doing things that would eliminate waste and add value to the customer. So when the opportunity arose to attend a daylong seminar to learn about a tool called "5S," I jumped for it.

5S is a process that helps in the organization and housekeeping of a business and provides a safer work environment. The 5S tool follows a five-step process:

1. **Sort**: determining necessary items from unnecessary,
2. **Straighten/Set in Order**: organizing items so there is a place for everything and everything in its place,
3. **Sweep/Shine**: sweeping the place visually and physically, and cleaning the work area,
4. **Schedule/Standardize**: creating a systematic method to maintain the condition accomplished in the first 3Ss, and
5. **Sustain**: following through with the commitment to maintain the changes to reduce waste.

Wow.

Here was a system that was not only easy to understand, but could establish a way to make sure it stays that way. Later you will read in detail of how we used this tool.

This kind of organization touched my personal passions for order and preparedness. I was intrigued and wanted to know more about Lean.

At its root, the Lean process is a common-sense approach. First, you need to understand what is required and organize the work in the most efficient manner. Then you apply best practices and spread the message. These ideas have been around for centuries. No doubt the builders of the pyramids incorporated such concepts. I wanted to learn more about enlarging this concept in the field of construction, to investigate further.

THE JOURNEY CONTINUES

At a trade association convention, I noticed a seminar advertising

Lean Construction. I attended the seminar, presented by LCI—the Lean Construction Institute, which focused on the Last Planner System™*. The Last Planner System emphasizes performing scheduled work more efficiently by eliminating work variation. This planning tool identifies what tasks need to be completed, when they are expected to be finished, and any obstacles that may arise requiring adjustments to the schedule *before* the actual work begins. The system creates a mechanism to discuss tasks with all key members of the project team; by doing so, it helps clarify who is working on what, where, and when.

The 5S's

Sort
Straighten / Set in Order
Sweep / Shine
Schedule / Standardize
Sustain

I learned of other companies involved in the Lean process. I visited a mechanical contractor that had applied some of the Lean principles and saw firsthand how 5S worked in a shop setting. Everything was neatly stored and identified with labels for easy access, and cleaning supplies were readily available—all resulting in maintaining a safer environment. I saw what the Lean process could accomplish. I began to search other areas regarding Lean Construction.

At this point, I had not found much information about Lean beyond the 5S principles. But as my journey continued, I discovered more tools of Lean available—indeed, an entire Lean toolbox.

At the Milwaukee School of Engineering, the Business Excellence Consortium (BEC) was advocating a training program to not only allow one to become acquainted with these principles, but actually become a master in them. As such, one could become the *sensei*, or champion, in one's own organization, assisting in the application of Lean principles throughout the whole organization. In the summer of 2003, I decided to embark on this educational program.

What I learned there gave me a much clearer understanding of and

---

*Last Planner is a registered trademark of the Lean Construction Institute.

appreciation for what the Lean process could accomplish. I was overwhelmed, and at the same time energized. In my classes, I met individuals not only from the local area but from other countries. Although their employers generally were manufacturers, and not construction companies, their experiences with Lean helped me realize the urgency for us to get on boardand sooner, not later.

BRINGING IT HOME

I approached Paul Grunau, the president of our company, Grunau Company, a full-service mechanical systems company and specialty metals fabricator, and gave him my vision: here, I told him, was an approach that would benefit us and differentiate us from other equally qualified mechanical contractors. Through the Lean principle of error-proofing, we would stop repeating the same mistakes over and over. Error-proofing is simply looking at a process in depth and devising how to make it *impossible* to make the same mistake again.

Here's a simple example: When you fill up at the gas station, it's impossible to put diesel fuel into a gasoline-powered car—because the nozzle on the diesel dispenser is too large to fit into the car's fuel filler tube.

Paul and I decided to incorporate these principles throughout the company so we could add greater value to our customers by eliminating waste in all possible venues of our business. As we read through dozens of publications on how companies could change over to Lean principles, one message became clear: this would be a long, continuous journey that would fundamentally require us to change the company culture, and to communicate as much to our team members.

Many other companies had failed to make the journey because they failed to view it as a long-term commitment, a journey requiring considerable time and continual effort. Unlike many businesses in the United States looking for short-term results every quarter, the business that is going to change to the Lean process must commit to months, even years, of continually scrutinizing its processes. And it must be willing to accept the challenge of continually striving to improve them.

Our journey could not be just a matter of slogans or a new program of the month. It meant that in order for us to succeed, a lot of thought had to go into what we were going to do.

PUTTING IT ON PAPER

Work on developing the vision of Lean Construction for our company began. I spent several days drafting that vision. As scheduling is a major element in the makeup of any construction company, I knew that we would have to have a timetable for implementing our Lean journey. The following is a portion of the final draft of our vision and the timetable for implementation:

> As a company, we are continually looking at various ways to provide greater value to our customers. In recent months, we have been involved with projects that are taking a different approach to the way jobs are managed. This different method of construction is referred to as "Lean Construction." The idea of "Lean" is not new. The concept dates back to the 1980s, when the automobile industry began using a different way of manufacturing.
>
> We became aware of "Lean Construction" in the fall of 2001. Subsequently we began trying to apply the principles on jobs in the local area. In addition, we have visited the facilities of a large mechanical contractor that has implemented some of the Lean principles.
>
> Lean thinking helps to clearly identify value, which is providing the best in both service and price through waste reduction. The main objective of Lean Construction is to reduce "work variation." The "work" involved here is not just in the field or shop operations, but transcends to all aspects of our business: estimating, engineering, purchasing, financial, information systems, and transportation.
>
> Lean Construction challenges long-standing practices in light of what has been done to revolutionize the manufacturing industries. The Lean

process is systematically applied to common sense. The Lean Production goals are as follows:

- Deliver the product, while . . .
- Maximize value (give the customer what they need when they need it) and
- Minimize waste (eliminate anything not needed for delivering value), and
- Pursue perfection (never stop striving to better achieve the Lean ideal)

As with any improvement, there will be a certain amount of change. Change is not always comfortable. However, in accordance with our Mission, we must constantly "measure and evaluate our performance with an open mind to change and continuous improvement." To that end, we will embark upon a long-term commitment to apply the principles of Lean in all aspects of our business. Ted Angelo will be responsible for the coordination/implementation of our "Lean Construction Initiative." Initially we are targeting the Milwaukee Branch. Shortly you will receive training in the principles of Lean Construction. A preliminary milestone schedule follows:

Timetable

- April/May/June 2003. Training of Lean principles and the 5Ss, Milwaukee, shops/field/office.
- July 2003. Implement 5Ss in one shop.
- August 2003. Complete design of mobile carts on jobs for all trades (standardize).
- December 2003. Mobile carts on jobs.
- February 2004. Identify "Lean" principles in engineering/project management.
- May 2004. Implement "Lean" principles in engineering/project management.
- June 2004. Identify "Lean" principles in purchasing.
- July 2004. Implement 5Ss in another shop (possibly sooner).
- September 2004. Implement "Lean" principles in purchasing.
- October 2004. Implement 5Ss in another shop (possibly sooner).

- January 2005. Identify "Lean" principles in financial/accounting/information systems.
- April 2005. Implement "Lean" principles in financial/accounting/information systems.
- September 2005. Implement 5Ss in remaining shops.
- January 2006. Complete implementation throughout the company.
- January 2007. Review all processes, make necessary changes/adjustments.

As you can see from the above, this is not a small task. A systematic approach will be taken. Not every area can be accomplished at the same time. We will need the commitment and cooperation of all members of the Grunau TEAM in order to make this the success it has the proven potential to accomplish. As our Mission states, we are devoted to "empowering our TEAM, allowing them to see how they each individually fit and add value." With this in mind, together, we look forward to making the Grunau Company the "benchmark of excellence" for the entire industry of what "Lean Construction" can do.

STEP-BY-STEP

Since Lean is founded on continual improvement, the initial timetable was developed to identify the main areas of our business where we would be concentrating on implementing the Lean principles. Once we had addressed each of these areas with our first wave, the plan called for us to return to each of the specific areas and reevaluate our newer processes with a view to continual change and improvement.

It was a measure of our naïve enthusiasm, as well as our natural instinct in the always-time-sensitive construction business, that we tried in the first year to schedule exactly what we would do week to week.

The complexities inherent in our business and in the construction industry in general soon showed up. Items took longer than anticipated to complete. Our work demands meant we couldn't have one person spending 100 percent of his time dedicated to the Lean process. We soon learned that we couldn't accurately schedule details down to a weekly basis at first; it took us from 2003 to the end of 2007 to realize our first year's vision.

The underlying principle in connection with the Lean journey was to help everyone appreciate that we, as a company, were always going to be trying to provide greater value to our customers. Value, though, is expressed in many different ways. We wanted to start with a focus on examining our various processes, with the idea of providing greater value by eliminating waste.

In keeping with our insight that it was extremely important to communicate to all team members or employees the need to understand what the Lean journey would look like, Paul Grunau and I issued the vision and timetable as a company-wide memo to all team members. We wanted to explain what we were going to do, what was going to be necessary for us to be successful, and what exactly we were going to try to accomplish.

KEEPING EVERYONE IN THE LOOP

Since change is difficult for many people, we felt it necessary to inform everyone. Most importantly, all needed to know it wasn't just a short-term fix or solution. In addition, it was necessary to help everyone understand that this change of culture to Lean principles was not just going to be in the office, in the field, or in the shop, but it would transcend all aspects of our business: estimating, engineering, purchasing, financial, information systems, and transportation.

We wanted to help everyone appreciate that this Lean thinking would challenge long-standing practices, just as it already had in revolutionizing manufacturing. So it was very important that this Lean process be recognized and that we show how it could be applied systematically throughout our business.

CHEERLEADER AND COACH

I became our in-house champion of the Lean process. One of the primary characteristics of any champion must be a burning desire to see the Lean process implemented throughout the organization. It is important that the individual or the champion be someone in a position to enact the changes and have the support of upper management. Since there will be critical changes, in some cases very different from the way we worked previously, the champion must touch base with all departments in the company, encouraging all not just to remain positive about the changes but to be enthusiastic, to really embrace them. As is true in any major endeavor, if top management is not behind an initiative within any business, it is very difficult for that initiative to succeed.

In addition, though, for change to be permanent, the individuals making the change must be convinced that there really *is* a better way of doing things. If management merely dictates and forces individuals to comply with a new program, it won't last. Team members as individuals, after some time, must come to appreciate that the Lean process will benefit not only the company but themselves.

In construction, perhaps the biggest concern that team members express—especially those out in the field and on the jobsite—is this: What jobs have we recently received? What they're really asking with this question is, "Where is *my* next job? How can I continue to support my family?"

For that reason, it was especially important for me, as the Lean champion, to convey to all of our team members, both in the field and in the office, that the Lean process will allow the company to continue to be competitive, resulting in attaining more work, which, in turn, provides jobs for our team members.

One of the keys to ensuring our success was effective, ongoing communication. We wanted everyone in the company to understand what we were trying to do. As we explained in the memo, we felt the best way to do this was through training. The next chapter will discuss how we went about this training process, as well as additional necessary steps involved in the journey of the implementation of our Lean vision.

2

Assessment & Training Program

Once the memo was issued, it was time to begin the implementation process. Attending courses in Lean manufacturing had helped us gain some knowledge of the concept, but when it came to the construction industry, we had much to learn.

For the next year, I attended every course on Lean principles available through the Milwaukee School of Engineering/BEC. My goal was to understand those principles and to develop a program for a construction company.

These were not the conventional courses taught at a college. Rather, they were courses taught at various locations, usually on the premises of large manufacturing companies. One such course, designed for making Lean presentations, drew students from Europe and other parts of the world. The interchange between the students from Europe and other countries woke me up to the reality that Lean manufacturing wasn't just an American fad—it was a worldwide phenomenon. That's when I got to know WCM Associates, a trainer in Lean manufacturing principles.

Professional Help

It was clear that to apply Lean to our industry, construction, we needed more help from outside resources. We hired a consultant, Larry Rubrich, the principal at WCM Associates, to assess our company and give us feedback on how to implement Lean principles in our company. When Larry was finished with his assessment, he came back to the company president and me.

"I have good news and bad news," he said.

I asked for the bad news first.

"What you are trying to implement within your company, you will not be able to find anyone in the construction industry that is trying to apply the Lean principles throughout their organization."

"What is the good news?" I asked.

"You can write the book."

So here it is.

Why Are We Here?

The assessment process included talking to a variety of people, trying to assess our current state and to identify potential roadblocks to our becoming a Lean enterprise. In one revealing question, Larry asked our team members, "What is it that the company expects you to do?"

The typical response: "To give a good day's work and do the best that I can in the course of an eight-hour day."

Sounds reasonable. Yet in construction, we are very detail-oriented. We plan out exactly what we need to accomplish for certain days, weeks, and months in order to finish an entire building or large complexes in an 18-to-24-month period. It became clear that we needed to look at trying to spend enough time with the team members so they understood that more was needed than just a generalization.

We needed to establish some benchmarks.

Communicating the Vision

One of the first benchmarks we had to establish as a company was to make sure that everyone understood our vision of Lean Construction. This was difficult. In the construction industry, especially in firms employing a number of different trades, the workforce fluctuates from time to time. Larry felt it was necessary to train all of the individuals within the company.

To bring everyone in for an initial training period required a very large investment of time and money, especially since our workforce varies in response to shifting workloads: new projects starting, old projects finishing, along with turnover in personnel hired through the unions to which our tradespeople belonged. We also knew that we would be training some individuals who might only be with us a short time.

Larry had suggested an eight-hour initial training. We felt that was more than we needed to educate the workforce on what Lean was all about—basically, eliminating waste. So we opted for four instead.

The training was a first for Larry, too: instead of the usual classroom of 25 to 30 that he was accustomed to, we trained much larger groups at a time. We had over 300 individuals in our field employment at that time, and we needed to spread the word quickly. We could only focus on individuals in a very limited way.

A PINPOINT FOCUS

It's important to understand that we weren't really concentrating on changing the process we had in place then. We were just focused on eliminating waste. In the training sessions, we asked team members what kind of waste they saw every day on the job: What are we doing now, and what could we be doing?

We got many different perspectives, reflecting the variety of people who took part in the training. At the same time, many of the points duplicated each other. No matter. When people raised their hands and identified a potential example of waste, we put it on the list. Everyone had an opportunity to chime in, and the result was a tremendous list with more than 200 individual items observed by people from across the company.

We heard from those who saw the problems directly on the job or in the office, and those whose function was to transmit information between the office and the field—something that, when people have to wait for information, can be the No. 1 source of waste in our industry.

One tradesman came up to me at the end of one of the sessions and said, "Ted, you have been in the business a long time, more than 25 years. Is there anything that we listed that was different, something that you had not heard before?" No, I admitted, "I have heard all of these before."

He challenged me: "Then what makes this Lean Construction any different than anything we've done before?"

And so I explained it to him: "What I have learned so far is that we're going to take a new approach. We will have teams assembled to look at these problems and come up with solutions—teams of people who are actually involved, not necessarily managers or executives, but rather people who are faced with the situations day in and day out. At the same time, we are going to have other people who are not involved with the type of work under analysis look at the situation with a separate set of eyes. They might be able to see some problem or area of waste more clearly, since they are looking at the work from a completely different perspective."

THE CONSTRUCTION DIFFERENCE

We did face one major challenge that continues to this day. Those who helped us understand these Lean principles focused the majority of their discussion on the manufacturing sector. Yet there are obvious, significant differences.

For example, manufacturing, for the most part, takes place in a controlled environment; construction is subject to day-to-day changes in weather, location, and other factors. So a major struggle during this early training was not only to help our people understand what Lean was, but also to help our instructors understand that there were some differences between manufacturing and construction.

Despite the differences, though, the Lean principles themselves could still be applied to construction. As in manufacturing, in the construction business, we *really* do perform the same thing over and over again; while manufacturers do so in the same location, we just do it in different locations. If the process is repeatable, then we should be able to apply the Lean principles: looking for ways to eliminate waste by examining the steps required to perform the process.

Change is extremely difficult in a construction setting. We give a lot of responsibility to individuals to guard our resources, both material costs and human resources. For the most part, team members in the field are left on their own to make decisions regarding their work methodology and practices.

A Challenge to Change

For people accustomed to such autonomy for so long, the project of examining and possibly changing all of our processes, regardless of how long or how well various individuals have been performing them, understandably can trigger a strong resistance to change.

Knowing that change would involve all types of personalities in our organization, we decided to form a Lean Steering Committee with varied personalities. Although we did chose them from different departments, the driving force in the selection was personality. The idea is that they would come up with a plan that would be understood and achievable with all types of individuals.

The Steering Committee consisted of seven people and included someone from each broad area of the company: shop, field team members, project management team, engineering group, accounting group, and service team. Representing the executive group was my executive assistant, and I acted as chair of the committee.

From time to time, we have rotated committee members in and out of the Steering Committee, but for constancy and continuity, we always kept six on the team: project manager, engineering manager, service manager, CFO, executive assistant, and myself as chair. At the same time, it was extremely important to have new blood on the committee so that those of us who remained on it for longer periods would not become complacent.

Assessment and training to implement our vision represents a very large investment, both in time and money. However, this investment was extremely important for us to establish what we were going to accomplish.

At the same time, there was no immediate return on this training. Some chief executives might look at the cost of bringing together a group of people and trying to inculcate in them a vision, and, seeing no immediate financial return, dismiss it as too expensive and a non-starter. Paul Grunau rightly viewed it differently: not as a cost, but an investment in the future.

As you read the chapters to follow, you will understand the importance of recognizing this as an investment with no immediate return. You must view it as a long-term commitment, and if you do, you will see that as individuals in your company, whether veterans or newcomers, come to understand these principles, the resulting cultural change will generate an immeasurable wealth of ideas.

That is why it was so important for us, from the start, to articulate our vision and then to train and help people understand our goal: to set ourselves apart from our competition by eliminating waste and concentrating on value.

3
First 5S Event: Tool Room

With the initial training behind us and the Steering Committee established, we felt ready to take the next step on our journey: our first Lean event. As I've already noted, from the very beginning, buy-in from upper management is critical for Lean to work. We had that at the Grunau Company; now it was necessary to ensure that the next level of management was also on board and could see the value of the Lean approach. Larry helped us appreciate that whatever the first Lean event would be, it should leave the participants with just one reaction: *Wow!*

Incidentally, there's no need to get hung up on the term "Lean event." You can call it *kaizen*, which means in Japanese "Continuous Improvement," as many do in Lean Manufacturing. Or you can use language that is unique to your company's culture. The important thing is for it to permeate your organization, by whatever name you give it.

The first Lean tool, and the foundation of all other Lean activities, is 5S. The 5S tool is nothing more than good housekeeping and organization in its simplest form. It involves 5 basic activities:

1. **Sort**
2. **Straighten/Set in Order**
3. **Sweep/Shine**

4. Schedule/Standardize

5. Sustain

Let's discuss those one at time.

SORT

- Items have a tendency to come into an area and stay so long they become part of the landscape. The first S gets the unnecessary items out of our way.
- It is necessary to sort through everything.
- Separate out both unneeded items and those in the wrong place.
- Remove these items from the work area.
- Add only what is needed.

STRAIGHTEN/SET IN ORDER

- Decide where to keep necessary items: have a place for everything and everything in its place.
- Organize how to keep them.
- Get items off the floor whenever possible.
- Make it easy to find items and use them.
- The more often an item is used, the closer it should be to where it is used.
- Every item should be labeled—making it obvious to everyone where it belongs.
- Keep safety in mind and make improvements to prevent injuries.
- Use lines and signboards to help show where things go.

SWEEP/SHINE

- Team members have responsibility to maintain their work area; this develops ownership.
- Cleaning is not as simple as making an area look good, but involves identifying problems early.
- Determine targets and assignments: who will perform the cleaning for the specific targets and the methods to be used?

- Determine cleaning methods; provide the right tools and supplies.
- Perform initial cleaning of everything: start the cleaning at the top and work down.
- Sweep also means to actually physically look over the area to ensure everything is in order.

SCHEDULE/STANDARDIZE

Now it is time to maintain and monitor the activities from the first 3Ss. **Standardize** refers to the condition you want your work area to be in—not an activity. The first 3Ss have been defined, and now you will establish a systematic method to maintain that condition. Document the process you established during the event.

- Cleaning standards are also set, including step-by-step instructions.
- Everyone must know exactly what he or she is responsible for doing (when, where, and how).
- Make the standards visual; make it easy to tell the difference between what is correct and incorrect.
- Color coding also makes identification easy.
- Create guidelines for using labels and signs.
- Ensure that the labels and signs make the workplace brighter and more orderly.
- Communication boards (white boards do a great job) for the area are an effective place to post this information.
- Document the process. If it is repeatable, find the best way to do it and continue to update as improvement is made.

SUSTAIN

5S is easy to do in the beginning, but it is hard to keep it going. To keep 5S going, it must be part of everyone's job, every day. **Standardize** and **sustain** are closely linked. To standardize, you set the rules for maintaining the 5S activity. By sustaining, you build the commitment to stick to the rules.

- Develop Monthly Audit Checklists.

- Identify who will perform the audit.
- Post the Audit and Cleaning Schedule.

As we examined our various departments in the office, out of the office, in our shops, and in the field, we decided that one of the most difficult areas in our business was supplying the correct and proper tools at the right time to the job.

For some 25 years of observing both jobsites in the field as well as jobs within the office and working around the country, it became clear to us that this area was ripe to be the focus of our first Lean event. Looking at the Tool Room, which I had been accustomed to seeing in disarray for 25 years, reinforced the idea. Larry helped us understand the importance of taking the time to thoroughly plan for our first event.

SELECTING THE TEAM

The next step to ensure success was selecting the correct team members. The selection process would be critical, knowing that change brings resistance. We wanted to guard against negative attitudes, especially because this would be our very first Lean event, and therefore our very first team.

The Steering Committee reviewed potential team members, and the No. 1 criterion was *a positive attitude*. Since this team would come from many different departments, we also took into consideration team members' willingness to go beyond the boundaries of their group. In addition, this team would consist of office and field personnel, individuals who would be meeting for the first time.

Clearly many factors were considered before selecting the first team. (Later, as future teams were selected, the task became easier.) For this first event, the Steering Committee reviewed the entire roster of personnel and discussed the qualifications of each before picking the team. First and foremost, we were looking for a positive attitude, a desire to learn new things, and a reputation to get things accomplished. The great deal of time this took was absolutely necessary for success.

One final factor we took into consideration in the selection process was influenced by the fifth S, Sustain. To sustain the process is by far the most difficult task to accomplish over time, as it truly requires self-discipline, especially by the individual who manages a particular area. Therefore, we saw the need to ensure that the manager of the department on which we focused was intimately involved from the beginning. So it was in our Tool Room event.

The Actual Event

The consultant warned us not to do any work related to the mission of the event prior to the event. For construction company team members, this is very different from the way we normally approach a job. Advance planning, and sometimes actual advance work, such as prefabricating a subunit or component to speed up later work on the jobsite, is not only standard, but required.

For a Lean event, however, it is very important to enable all team members to be totally involved in the decision-making process.

There was preparation, though. We had to look first at the way we conducted our business—in this case, the way we worked every day in the Tool Room—so that we could establish the parameters, or objectives, for the team.

The first step was to look at the layout of the Tool Room. We created a so-called "spaghetti diagram" illustrating what it takes to fill the typical order. (It's called a spaghetti diagram because when it is finished, the lines and arrows that describe the tasks involved look like a bowl of spaghetti.). We then counted *every* step physically required in order to fill that order: 525 steps.

In all of our events, including this one, we tried to set a reduction goal. If we really wanted to stretch, that goal would be to cut the steps by 50 percent. For the Tool Room, our goal was to reduce the steps to 263 by rearranging the way the equipment, tools, and consumables were located.

On several occasions, as the Steering Committee continued to prepare for this first event, we had to resist the temptation to do some preliminary work. However, we were reminded that we weren't just here to transform the Tool Room: we were also training future Lean event teams.

THE IMPORTANCE OF TRUST

If we were going to convince our people that this Lean journey really was a journey together, not just a program, and that it really was something different, not just management telling individuals what to do, we needed to trust the team explicitly to make the decisions about what to do during the event. Therefore, we did nothing until the team was formed and set its own strategy and tasks for the Tool Room event. You can imagine there was a lot of anxiety about the outcome.

The event was five days long. The first day consisted of training. We brought the team up-to-date with the preliminary data that we had gathered so that they could understand the objectives for this event and what was needed to meet them, specifically reduce the number of steps by 50 percent. Along with the four hours of reviewing the data, we included a training session explaining the 5S principles. It is important to remember that these principles are not revolutionary—they're just plain, good old housekeeping.

As stated in our training, the 5S principles can and will be applied to every area within the company: not just the field or, in this case, the Tool Room, but in the office, in our shop areas, in our trucks—everywhere. The 5S principles can even apply in our homes. (A word of advice, though: If you're going to bring these principles home, first make sure you have complete agreement from your spouse—if you want a continued relationship, that is! Just ask my wife!)

Once the objectives and the data supporting them were clear, the second portion of the training day was used to brainstorm ideas with the team to solicit their ideas for meeting those objectives. Once all the ideas were categorized, the team voted on the top five or 10 items that they deemed critical to meet the objectives. Once the top five or 10 items were identified, we then began to formulate what it was we were going to do in the next three-and-a-half days.

Why not four? Half of Day 5 was reserved for the entire team to develop a "Report Out," that is a presentation to be given to the management group on what was accomplished that week. The presentation would report on the objectives and whether or not they were met, and include pictures taken during the event. Each team member would outline what had been accomplished and field questions from the management group.

Sorting out the Lessons

One question Paul Grunau consistently asked was, "What will you take back to your job next week that you have learned from participating in this event?" The importance of this question was to convey once again that it wasn't just about the event that week: the overarching goal was to change the whole culture of the company, so that the principles learned in the event could be carried through and implemented throughout the company regardless of where the individual worked.

At the conclusion of this first event, when Paul walked into the completely redesigned and organized Tool Room, his first words were completely spontaneous: "WOW, what a difference!" The Tool Room had been transformed from a disorganized, dimly lit room to a bright, clean center where the tools were easy to find, as they were organized in a manner similar to grocery aisles—labeled and identified.

You could not have had a better reaction as far as those of us on the Steering Committee were concerned. We wanted the rest of the company to understand what can be done in a very short time by harnessing not only the physical labor of a team, but also their mental and emotional resources. This team of 15 individuals from all aspects of our business cooperated, and by the end of the week, had formed a special bond.

Quite frankly, it is easy to organize an area according to 5S. The most difficult part—but the most important, indeed in the foundation

TOOL ROOM BEFORE

of the Lean journey—is to *maintain* what was accomplished during that short time. That's why the fifth S is **sustain**, or self-discipline: making sure that the effort put forth to first organize the area was matched in keeping the new way of doing things going.

To that end, we developed an audit program and an appropriate audit form. We would regularly audit areas that had been through a Lean reorganization, looking at the conditions on the day of the audit and scoring various items on a scale of 0 to 4 (worst to best). The audit looked at the individual 5Ss: whether everything was sorted properly, straightened in place, shined or cleaned, and whether the standard processes were being followed. The audit process reinforced the 5S mindset and was extremely helpful to guarantee success.

LEARNING TO TRUST THE TEAM

Every event requires a facilitator with no biases about the outcome. We felt it was necessary on this first event to have an outside consultant to ensure success. For all other events, due to my additional training, I

TOOL ROOM AFTER

facilitated events.

This was often challenging for me. Having been a project engineer, manager of operations, manager in the office, and on remote jobsites, it was extremely difficult for me not to influence the decisions made by the various teams. But I repeatedly reminded myself that *the team decision is the best decision.*

Why? If your team reflects the true diversity of your workforce, with a variety of individuals with varying backgrounds, and if it has at the same time received very clear objectives, the team's decisions will be best suited to help the many types of personalities, who work in your firm adhere to those decisions.

We had established a baseline and set specific goals for improvement in the Tool Room. Now it was time to revisit the goals to see how close we came to accomplishing them. One goal was to reduce the number of steps required to fill a typical order by 50 percent. After the 5S Lean event, we filled the same typical order and measured the steps . . . 262! We had met our goal.

Better still, in the year after the event, we saved $59,000 on new tools that we *didn't* have to buy because our better-organized Tool Room also had fostered a better system of repairing existing tools. A computerized tracking system to locate tools on the jobsite or in storage enabled us to make use of the tools we already had and reduced the need to buy new ones. WOW!

We also had installed in our Tool Room a graphic showing the cost of tools per man-hour and the relationship between hours in the field and the cost of purchased tools (see below). By focusing our attention on supplying tools more efficiently to jobsites, we met our goal of reducing tool costs even though our man-hours would increase.

TOOL ROOM MATRIX

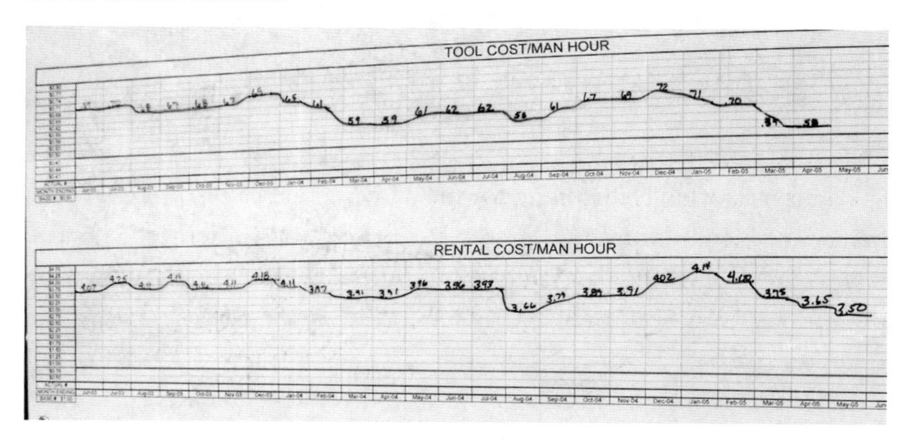

With our first event under our belt, so to speak, and such a grand success, we felt confident to continue our Lean journey with more 5S events. With each one, our confidence in the Lean processes, as well as our ability to adapt it to a construction setting, naturally grew. The next chapter will discuss five of these 5S events and demonstrate more of the Lean principles in action.

4 Other 5S Events

Cleaning Up Our Yard

Fresh from our victory with the Tool Room event, the next Lean event was the Yard event. Many construction companies, especially contractors who use their own personnel rather than hiring subcontractors, find that when a job is complete, leftover material returns to the contractor's shop or yard. Over time, quite a mix and quantity of items accumulate, until it can be difficult, if not impossible, to see just what's in inventory.

Doing a 5S event on the Yard made perfect sense. Lean is all about eliminating waste. I can't count how many times I had seen workers come to the yard and look through crates and crates of material searching for a specific item to be used on the job, only to find out the item was not in any of the many boxes.

Simply put, time is money: since field labor is a large component of our cost, it is apparent that having the material organized is far less costly than having it scattered about, with workers constantly going on fruitless treasure hunts that may take minutes or hours, only to find out that the material must be purchased after all.

Seen this way, it becomes clear that sending material back to the supplier is much more cost-effective than transporting it back to the yard or shop: if there's no stockpile to begin with, the time-wasting treasure hunts never begin.

There's another benefit. If by some chance the material is in the stockpile, we pay the cost—in labor, fuel, and time—of transporting it to the jobsite. By contrast, if we just purchase the material as required, it is delivered to the individual or job by the supplier. Therefore, the cost of getting the material to the location of installation is borne by

YARD BEFORE

YARD AFTER

the supplier and not the individual worker.

For the Yard event, we used the same basic process as we had for the Tool Room event: The first day was dedicated to training and brainstorming ideas to establish the goals to meet our objectives.

Day 2 began with applying the first of the 5S principles:—**sort**. This was a huge job to undertake; our company had accumulated more than *30 years* worth of materials that had been brought back to the yard from previous jobs. Team members debated what materials, if any, could possibly be used in the near future.

Of course, then we had to continually define what we meant by "near future." "But if we throw this out," someone would say, "you know for sure next week someone will need it!" Over the course of three days, the team continued this evaluation process—and ended up throwing out 75 percent of the material that had been stored. What remained was then sorted properly and identified in order to ensure no more treasure hunts.

TACKLING THE WAREHOUSE

As you can imagine, the impact of this event was as dramatic as the previous one. By now, excitement was beginning to grow among our team members, and more people were interested in volunteering for the next 5S event.

The next event took place in the company Warehouse, an area 50 feet wide by 125 feet long. As with the Yard, material stored in the Warehouse had been there for decades. Our company had developed an annual routine in which I would lead a group of project managers through the Warehouse on a Saturday morning to identify materials and equipment they thought would be used in the coming year. And every year, year after year, the same group would identify the same equipment or material that they were sure would be used.

We had to do something different.

As with the other events dealing with chaos that had grown over a long time, the sorting process was time consuming. But it was also worth it: we were able to sort out what was not needed from what was needed and reduced the occupied floor space by 50 percent.

The now-vacant area was later used by our Sheet Metal Department to increase production. Again we asked ourselves whether or not we really needed this piece of equipment or that stack of material. Applying the fourth of the 5S principles—**schedule**—we also began dating all of the equipment and material located in the Warehouse. This allowed us to identify items that had been in the Warehouse for some time and not used.

Sorting and straightening are ongoing processes, and they require a diligent effort to keep the material and equipment under control. Once again, as we had in the Tool Room and in the Yard, we executed the fifth S by compiling information, dating materials and equipment, and regularly employing the audit, so that we could control the accumulation and organization of equipment and material in the Warehouse.

A LESSON IN CONSENSUS

It was during our initial brainstorming for the Warehouse event that something happened to help me appreciate the value of getting consensus, especially in the planning stages. We had to answer a seemingly small question: how long would we retain something in the warehouse before discarding the item?

The majority of the team agreed on six months. One person, however, thought it should be less. Wanting to hasten the process, I said we would use a period of six months as our gauge for discarding unused material and equipment. As I began moving to the next item of discussion, the dissenter pushed back: "We did not get consensus," he said—I had simply *decided* it would be six months.

He was right. I backtracked, and we spent the next 40 minutes trying to reach consensus and wound up reducing the six months to five months.

Was this a lot of time wasted? No. The point was not about the

Warehouse Before

Warehouse After

time used to reach consensus, but, rather, whether we would allow *the team* to make the decision as opposed to *management.*

Not long ago, I was discussing another issue with this same individual unrelated to the Warehouse situation. He made the comment we "should just go ahead and make a decision and get it done." However, I reminded him of the process we used when he was adamant about reaching a consensus. He then acknowledged with appreciation the time spent discussing this issue.

This illustrates the need to always be aware of and consider everyone's thoughts before making a decision. There is one caveat, though: remembering that our ultimate goal is to eliminate waste, we need to remember to exercise balance. The time of many team members shouldn't be unduly wasted for the sake of one person.

DISCERNING DISSENT

Occasionally you will find a team member who blocks consensus, not out of real concern for the issue at hand or the interests of the team but out of selfish preoccupation with himself and his ideas. It may be necessary to take this team member aside to help him see the need to focus on the team objective.

The work of the Warehouse event team and another team, the Vendor team, allowed our company to reduce the staff in the warehouse by one person. That person was reassigned. It is not our desire to eliminate team members when driving waste out of the business. If we let that happen, we would not continue to receive excellent suggestions to improve our processes.

Also, because we standardized material purchases and delivery, we reduced material handling in the Warehouse. This has saved us $60,000 to $100,000 *every year* since 2004 as well as enabled us to recapture 2500 square feet of floor space that was later used for production.

BUILDING ON OUR SUCCESS

We followed this event with three more 5S events in the Plumbing

PLUMBING PREFABRICATION BEFORE

PLUMBING PREFABRICATION AFTER

Pre-fabrication shop, the Weld shop, and, finally, Miscellaneous Metals. Each one was conducted in the same manner, and we saw good results from them all.

With every event, we followed a similar day-to-day routine. Here's the typical schedule. We met each morning at 7 a.m. over a breakfast of juice, coffee, and rolls. Teamwork sessions ran from 7 a.m. until a 9:30 a.m. break. During the break, the team assembled and discussed what had been performed that morning and reviewed the schedule of work to be done from 9:45 a.m. to noon. The team then had lunch as a group, reviewed the schedule for the rest of the day, and then carried it out.

This same routine was followed for each succeeding day of the event, with the time after lunch on the final day used to prepare the Report Out presentation for management. The presentation consisted of slides taken prior to or during the events—before and after pictures—as well as a review of the objectives of the team and the specific, quantifiable results. As part of the presentation, each individual member of the team prepared a minute or two of explanation and

WELD SHOP BEFORE

analysis of what he or she had gained from their participation on the team.

Converting a Skeptic

By now, we had established a certain rhythm for our 5S events. The enthusiasm was still good, and the stress of the unknown was easing off. We were becoming comfortable with the principles of Lean. Our company culture was starting to change. As we worked through the Miscellaneous Metals event, we could see directly how people were coming to understand the Lean process.

Weld Shop After

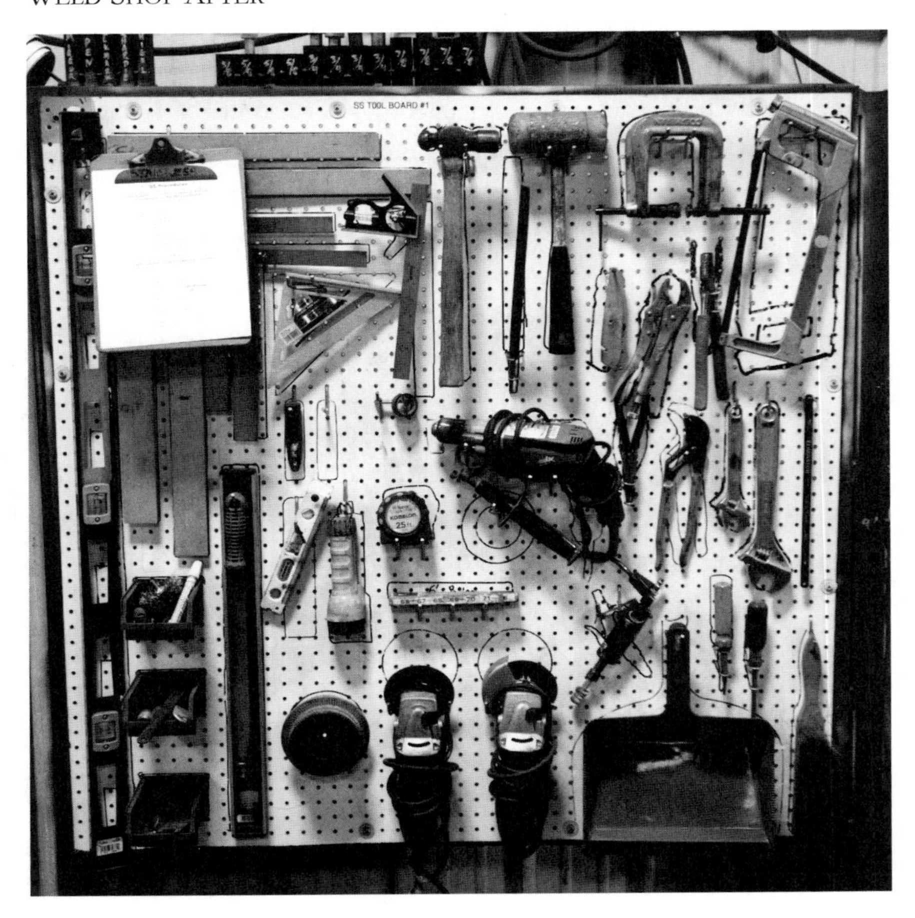

Our company, in addition to providing mechanical and fire protection services for buildings, also designs and fabricates miscellaneous metal building components: railings, stairways, tanks, wind tunnels, silos, light structural members, and the like.

Before the Miscellaneous Metals event, one particular tradesman—who had been "volunteered" by the committee instead of volunteering himself—wasn't shy about his skepticism, telling coworkers, "I will do what they want me to do, but I'm not offering any suggestions."

I wasn't aware of his comment before or during the event, but only was informed of it later, after the event was over. Sure enough, though, his initial involvement on the first day of training and brainstorming was lukewarm.

Yet during the brainstorming session, as we began listing all the items we wanted to accomplish and voted on the top 10, his mood changed, and he became more engaged. Understanding that the tasks the team set out to accomplish in the next three to four days were set by his team members appeared to make a difference to him.

MISCELLANEOUS METALS BEFORE

All of our events and all of our teams draw representation from a variety of different departments, which include both men and women. During this event, a woman from the Accounting department was working one-on-one with this skeptical tradesman. Part of the event included a small welding job that any of the tradespeople on the team could have accomplished.

This tradesman, however, took the initiative and opportunity to teach the accountant how to weld two pieces of metal together. Over the five-day event, with recurring team meetings for breaks and lunch, a spirit of camaraderie and a bond developed among team members. On the last day of the event, while we were preparing the presentation, this tradesman took it upon himself to make a special certificate for his fellow team member, certifying that she was an "official tacker," qualified to tack two pieces of metal together.

So this individual, who was going to do only what he was told to do, instead became very much engaged, not only in the work to be done but in the camaraderie of the team.

MISCELLANEOUS METALS AFTER

It didn't stop there. The Miscellaneous Metals Lean team had one outstanding task: remodeling the lunchroom used by the Metals division. This tradesman enthusiastically took part in the project. He now understood that we were interested in the team members and their ideas. We were even willing to take on the added cost of the lunchroom upgrade: it was something the team had decided and management approved, and the task was accomplished.

Persisting in Our Vision

There are many other such stories along our Lean journey, and they have built support and encouragement throughout our organization to keep the journey going, even in the face of individual skepticism and apathy.

Experiences like this give me faith that with patience and understanding, even some of the most diehard individuals with preconceived ideas can change and see the value of this work, not only for the company but for themselves as individuals. We can never give up our efforts in promoting our new culture, despite setbacks along the way.

The next chapter will deal with a new tool from the Lean toolbox: Value Stream Mapping.

5 Value Stream Mapping

This chapter deals with a different tool in the Lean toolbox: Value Stream Mapping. It's one of the more complicated tools we use. I will explain what it is and how to use it, and, finally, show an example of how we have used it effectively.

Picturing Our Processes

Value Stream Mapping is creating a one-page picture, or "Value Stream Map" (VSM), of every single process that occurs in a company. For example, from the time a customer places the order until the customer has "received the product"—in other words, the work is completed—Value Stream Maps document all the processes and steps used to complete the work.

Those steps include both those that add value and those that don't. We have another word for that second group of processes: waste. The goal of the VSM is to depict every aspect of work: the flow of material, the flow of information, the flow of services across and through all the processes required to complete the customer's work.

This is not a new concept. Henry Ford is credited with introducing process mapping as early as the 1920s to graphically display everything happening in a series of operations. The Japanese, and Toyota in particular, are credited with refining and perfecting "value stream mapping," which they also call "material and information flow mapping."

Why is value stream mapping such a valuable tool?

- It reduces the risk of creating "islands of excellence," in which individual steps of the process may be better and better, but we have failed to improve the **total system efficiency** of the **total value stream's** capability for customer satisfaction.
- It helps break down communication barriers.
- It identifies waste so it can be eliminated, thereby improving customer satisfaction.
- It creates a vision of the future by uncovering waste and opportunities to create flow—and making them visible to all.
- It enables broad participation in shaping the future.
- It offers a concrete starting point for improvement: once the "as-is," or "Current State," VSM is created, it becomes the baseline for creating the "Future State" VSM.
- And it offers a clear road map: the Future State VSM.

FOUR STEPS TO VALUE STREAM MAPPING

1. Pick a process to map (improve)
2. Create the "Current State" VSM
3. Create the "Future State" VSM
4. Develop an action plan to make the FSVSM the CSVSM

Careful consideration is vital when selecting the first process on which to try Value Stream Mapping. Why? As with any tool in the Lean toolbox, when the tool is first used, you want to make sure that the process you are trying to improve will result in a success and clearly show others the importance of this particular tool.

If the process you select is too complicated, mapping it can quickly become overwhelming. That can sour attitudes toward what can be an excellent tool when properly implemented. So start with a simple, uncomplicated process as your first Value Stream Mapping project.

HOW IT WORKS

Value Stream mapping begins by creating a flow chart of material, information, and services for a specific process. For each step in the process, you then establish the actual time it takes to accomplish it. This is called the Saw Tooth timeline.

Assigning specific times to the various steps enables us to identify the time that you consider *value-added* versus the time that you classify as *non-value-added*. Again, value-added time is the time spent on the process for which the customer is willing to pay. An example of non-value-added time is waiting for information or transportation of material that neither changes the shape nor adds any value to the process.

Ultimately you cannot eliminate *all* non-value-added time. For instance, material may have to be moved from one point to another; even though nothing is added to the material, the fact remains the material must be transported in order for the customer to receive the items. Such time is "non-value-added but necessary."

As you examine each non-value-added item in the VSM, look first at those non-value-added items that are *not* necessary before looking at the non-value-added *but* necessary items. It's also important initially not to over-complicate the Value Stream Mapping process as you complete the Current State map; it's more important at this stage to simply make sure you have identified *all* the steps involved. Labeling them as "value-added" or "non-value-added" can wait a bit, because some steps will jump out as non-value-added immediately. This is important in order for you to determine what steps may be eliminated even before looking at the non-value-added steps.

EXPERTS AND OUTSIDERS

As in any other Lean event, you will have to select team members.

Those who are intimately involved in the process must be a part of mapping it. A Value Mapping team may include as few as two or three people or as many as 10 or 12.

For example, in one of our departments, because all 10 department members were involved with bits and pieces of their department's process, all were involved in identifying steps involved in the current Stream. It is also helpful to have someone not involved in the process to provide a different perspective, to ask important questions such as, "Why do you do that?"

Prior to beginning the actual Value Stream process, assemble the team and train its members on how this tool is used. This would include explaining what Value Stream Mapping involves.

It will also include a very specific instruction: During the process of mapping the Current State, team members must concentrate on the *current situation*. This is *not* the time to get sidetracked by well-meaning team members who want to jump ahead and discuss ways to improve the current process. Those discussions end up bogging down the mapping process, making it very difficult to complete in a timely manner.

"LIGHTNING BOLTS"

You overcome this potential interference with "lightning bolts." As a process step is identified and someone pipes up, "Wait, why don't we change that step by doing x?" mark that step on the white board or with a sticky note. That way you can assure someone that their comments are appreciated, while staying on track with the task immediately at hand of simply mapping the current state.

Training for the VSM process needs to forcefully and clearly make the point that this is the best way to get through the current Value Stream. Later, when the Current State is complete and the Future State is being developed, the team can return to discussing the ideas—the lightning bolts—that were identified earlier.

SEEING THE FUTURE

Once the Current State map is completed, move on to the next step, Future State mapping. Before starting the Future State, go back and review all the steps that were identified. In fact, my experience has shown that it is beneficial to constantly review the steps as you are developing the Current State to ensure that no steps are missed.

Once all the steps are identified and you have identified "lightning bolts" that suggest ways to improve them, the next logical task is to identify which steps are obvious candidates for elimination requiring no lengthy discussion. Then you are ready to review the number of "lightning bolts" and determine which you can implement in the Future State.

You will find that it's very difficult when creating the first future map to incorporate all new ideas. Instead, you must become accustomed to thinking of the future map—in fact, our entire way of conducting business—as something you can always subject to continuous improvement.

Once you have reviewed the "lightning bolts" and determined what you want the Future State to look like, and you have buy-in from all of those involved, you need to communicate the results to others who may be affected by the new future map.

JOB ONE: COMMUNICATION

As you strive to make the Future State the Current State VSM, it is vital to exercise care and communicate clearly. Everyone will be affected by the efforts to move to an improved Future State, so all of those involved in the process, along with VSM team members, must be a part of the kick-off meeting to implement the change to the Future State.

This meeting should:

- Inform everyone what was learned in the process.
- In a non-threatening manner, inform everyone what steps will be followed to implement the suggested changes.
- Ask workers for any comments they may have on new

processes that the team might have overlooked.

Other tasks involved in making the Future State VSM (FSVSM) the Current State VSM (CSVSM) are equally important, but some are often overlooked. For example, it is very important to conduct regularly scheduled meetings for all participants, to provide a structure for the team to work on problem solving and complete tasks, and to periodically inform the Lean Steering Committee of the progress made.

KEEPING THE GOAL IN FOCUS

One additional step is extremely important, especially in changing not only procedures, but the culture of your company as well: continuously verify the progress on goals and support for the process. This is typically done by the Lean Steering Committee. To accomplish this, a simple approach for a top-level "Team Report-out" is to conspicuously post three VSMs:

1. The original Current State
2. The desired Future State
3. Where the team stands now

Think about that last map as a "virtual Current State VSM"—reflecting current performance. Comparing the three VSMs can speak volumes on progress you have already made and where more focus is needed.

A LESSON FROM A SUPPLIER

Through our experiences in implementing Lean, VSM has been an extremely useful tool. Here's just one example: we were having a recurring problem with the flow of material from one of our suppliers. I wanted to get to the bottom of it.

To discuss how we might get materials to a jobsite more quickly and efficiently, I met with the supplier's branch manager, regional director, and corporate director. They were aware of the problems we were experiencing, but they were surprised when I presented an overview of our Lean process.

Rather than beat them up at the meeting, I suggested we form a team made up of people from our two firms. They agreed.

The team consisted of four members from each company. It included those closest to the process: those actually involved in placing an order, receiving the order, and, finally, transferring the items to the warehouse to fill the order. The team would meet once a week for about a month. They would create a VSM and identify areas that required improvement.

At the very first meeting, we got some eye-opening information: the supplier's team members explained to us that a large number of the times when our workers picked up items from them, our people hadn't called in ahead of time. That meant our people were waiting around at the supplier's location while the supplier's team members worked to fill the order—a real waste of time.

We hadn't set out to identify waste in the way we placed our orders, but our partner helped identify a major source of wasted time on our part.

To identify how much time could be wasted by not calling ahead, I tried a little experiment. During one of our 5S truck events, explained in greater detail in Chapter Nine, we needed items from a supplier about five minutes from our shop. I did not call ahead. When I entered the supplier warehouse, two counter team members were helping two customers. I waited about 15 minutes before being helped. The supplier's clerk checked to see that what I needed was in stock, I gave a purchase number, and the team member went to the warehouse to pull the order.

After placing the material in our truck, I headed back to our shop. The total elapsed time was 35 minutes.

Several weeks later, we worked on another truck event. This time I called ahead of time, ordered the material, gave a purchase order number, and asked when it would be ready for pickup. The call took less than five minutes. I drove to the supplier, went directly to will call, and drove back to the shop.

The total time was 17 minutes—a 50 percent reduction! I had met with our supplier to help him with his problem, and he had helped us see a problem of our own that needed correction.

Taiichi Ohno, developer of the Toyota Production System, once said, "Eliminating waste is not the problem, identifying it is." That's the bottom-line lesson from Value Stream Mapping. As we travel along the Lean journey, we find again and again that since you never know where waste will be found, Value Stream Mapping is an essential tool in streamlining our processes and identifying sources of waste.

VALUE STREAM MAP

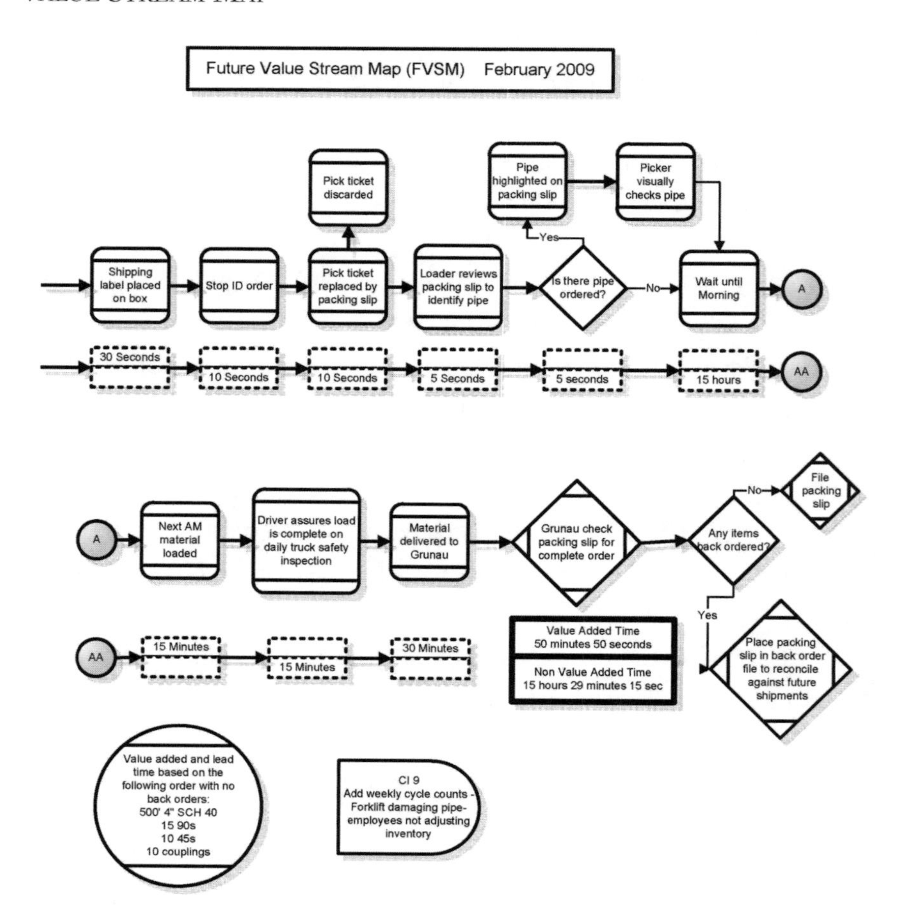

6 Service Department Event

Up to this time, most of our journey had focused on our shops, warehouse, and field operations. In early 2005, we began to spread the Lean philosophy and techniques into our company's office environment. We decided first to focus on a specific section, the Service Sales Department. This department is responsible for client relationships, garnering work, and dispatching our various tradespeople to customers' facilities.

The service area accounted for 15 percent of the total office space, but this event turned out to be much more important, paving the way for a much larger reorganization of the entire 22,000-square-foot office.

A New Kind of Team

For this event, we took a somewhat different approach, changing the composition of the team. What we were doing involved everyone in the department, so we decided to include everyone in the department on the team, rather than just a small group representing the larger unit. It was the largest team yet, and required us to spend much time talking about the different processes.

It was well worth it, because it helped everyone to see the total picture. Discussing the various tasks associated with each individual's processes both helped team members build a better appreciation for each other and fostered a coming together of minds to successfully achieve the team's common goals.

The team's overall objective was to look at the entire operations of the Service Department, including all the processes in which documents were filed and retrieved. The objectives were stated as:

Improvement Objectives/Goals/Benchmarks

- Document the processes of the individuals and the interplay of the entire team.
- Revisit profitability by Technician performing the job estimated by Salesman.
- Identify expectations for all team members.
- Improve flow through Service Department—both physical flow of job documentation and cubical layout.
- Labeling of area, files, etc. (visual communication)
- Identify all information; standardize how all information is maintained (by individuals, bids, files, etc.)
- Identify best-suited location for material and equipment.
- Visual Production Board—utilize handheld electronic tools.
- Accuracy—review rebilling issues.
- Streamline work order process—review flows from initial phone call to e-mail to Technician. How do we ensure all and correct information is entered?
- Use of contract module for preventive maintenance.
- Additional improvements/ideas by team.
- Develop and track time issues with work orders—from open close, from open to actual start, etc.
- Develop better filing of Operation & Maintenance Manuals in Service area.

Quantitative Goals

- Reduce number of rebillings.

- Reduce number of steps by 50 percent (two steps = one second).
- Identify jobs running over budgeted hours.
- Track and reduce where we have to return to rework jobs.

After establishing these goals and objectives, the team spent considerable time creating a Current State Value Stream Map of the Service Department's activities. Taking the time to understand the details of the current state of the business is never accomplished quickly. For this especially large team, it took a number of meetings with the entire team to fully map the existing process.

It was only then that the team thoroughly understood where improvements could and should be made. That process helped produce the list of objectives above, which then became the guideline for keeping the team focused on the more important items and making needed changes.

THE IMPORTANCE OF A BASELINE

I've already said this, but it's so important I can't say it too much: before starting any improvement, you must know what the baseline currently is. After all, how can you measure improvement without knowing where you started?

There's almost no such thing as too detailed. Consider this: part of the process of eliminating waste in any process is directly related to eliminating wasted physical steps.

With that in mind, the Service Department's manager literally began counting every step he took throughout the day. With this baseline information on his processes, he then shared the results with his team members. Simply by moving his work station from the far end of the department to the middle of the office space, he reduced the number of steps by over 50 percent!

You might ask, "Well, with e-mail, can't he just spend a lot less time walking to his team members?" On paper, that's true. But e-mail will never completely take the place of face-to-face meetings. You can't see the expressions, the demeanor, of your colleagues through an e-mail.

That brings up a larger point. Whenever you are searching for ways to eliminate steps, you must never become so obsessed with reducing them that you eliminate understanding and contact with your most prized of all resources: your people.

DISCOVERING A HIDDEN TALENT

As the manager and the rest of the team continued to establish the baseline for the Service Department operations, it became clear that the whole department needed to be reorganized. Not only would this add additional space for new sales personnel, it would also enhance communication.

It was during the discussion of this process that the idea really took hold of putting all the decisions about the Service group's office layout in the hands of the team, instead of just the manager. The team was asked to provide a new layout for the Service Department by the next meeting. Meetings were usually held weekly for about an hour. That

SERVICE DEPARTMENT BEFORE

weekend, an associate on the team went home and on Saturday morning, at the kitchen table, began to lay out what she thought would be the best design for the space.

People who work for contractors have a pretty good handle on how things should be arranged, so you can appreciate there was a great variety of ideas. But when they were all presented and the team voted on which new layout would work best—you guessed it: her layout was used.

Whenever I give a tour of our facilities, I always stop at her desk and explain to the visitors how she was intimately involved in the process of redesigning the Service Department space. She has gone on to help us streamline operations in other branches of the company. It is truly amazing what resources you already have but don't realize, unless you create an environment that allows everyone to express themselves in open, honest dialogue without fear of ridicule.

This would not have been possible if the Service Manager had not understood the team concept. As a facilitator of this group, I know

SERVICE DEPARTMENT AFTER

firsthand how important it is for the manager to not just pay lip service to the Lean process, but to actively encourage and promote the team and its ideas instead of his own.

A SALESMAN'S EPIPHANY

Here's another example of the value of having the team discuss each individual's processes and the impact that such discussion can have on the final outcome. One salesman with a long history at the company, someone who had always been very conscientious and profitable, thought the idea that everyone would have to file their jobs and estimates in the same manner seemed ridiculous. He had done just fine for all those years using his own methods; changing that struck him as silly.

However, as the weeks went by and further discussions ensued, it became clear that when this salesman was out of the office, his coworkers had a hard time answering his customers' questions or examining his files for needed, relevant information to respond to inquiries. This was especially problematic when the customer was on the phone and wanting a response right then and there.

Once it was explained how a common system of tracking jobs and filing information would benefit **his** customers, it began to make sense, and he was able to agree with the team and help establish consensus on the new process. Another believer! Today he is very much a proponent of the Lean process.

Our success with the Service Department was so powerful that it led us not only to consider, but also to undertake a project remodeling the entire office, implementing Lean principles as we went. I will discuss the entire office space remodel in the following chapter.

7
Office Remodel

The success of the Service Department event motivated us to take on perhaps the most far-reaching event we ever attempted. The actual event took place much later on our journey, in January 2007. The company headquarters was bursting at the seams. We lacked the space to properly house everyone and everything used in daily business. We had even eliminated our training room to accommodate additional personnel.

In addressing this dilemma, we explored a number of options: building a new building, leasing additional space close to the existing building, and remodeling the existing building. We decided to remodel, since it would be the most cost-effective means to accomplish our objective.

The objective was to provide a place for all current team members, including those who were sharing a space, and to provide a training room accommodating 40 people. We also wanted to provide space for an additional 20 percent growth in people, space, filing, and storage. This was a very daunting proposal, as part of the team's objectives included not expanding the building: we had to do everything within the existing four walls.

A Contentious Process

Early in 2006, we selected our team to orchestrate this project. This would be the most diverse of all teams we'd ever created. It also turned out to be the most contentious.

The team was made up of engineers, project managers, executives, administration staff, and support staff, both men and women. Despite the variety of personalities represented in this team, very many of them turned out to be classic "Type-A" people: each of them opinionated and very direct.

Seeing the mix of this particular team, we knew right away we would have to establish groundrules and stick to them: everyone should respect each other, hear what the others have to say, and take special care not to say something that would stifle the initiative of other team members. You can guess that for many of us, this wasn't how we were accustomed to communicating our ideas—to put it mildly!

An especially contentious issue was deciding how offices would be distributed among team members under the new design. Some of the team members had their own offices and were accustomed to that. Others worked in cubicles in the open workroom. You can imagine the number of heated discussions that took place when it seemed necessary to eliminate some offices in order to meet our objectives for the new design.

Many meetings passed with very little progress, and the conflict repeatedly resurfaced, slowing our progress. The team slogged on through the usual event steps, however, and by the time the brainstorming step was completed in April 2006, it had a list of 87 items to consider (some of them duplicates).

The team tried many different things to accommodate the various concerns of its members, while staying true to the original list of objectives. For example, in a sincere attempt to be as realistic as possible, some in offices or cubicles started to tape off certain parts of their work space to put up temporary physical barriers just to see what sort of work space they could really live with. Through this sort of trial-and-error approach, the team concluded that for most workers, a U-shaped desk configuration would work best. The exception was in Accounting, where an L-shape worked best.

The Office/Cubicle Turf War

Some of the team members who were accustomed to offices raised the very real issue that they needed privacy to carry on confidential conversations. The team leader suggested that everyone with an office currently keep track of how many times he or she had to close the door for confidential matters. This was comparable to the creation of a "Current State Value Stream Map" showing the baseline of what the real, everyday situation was.

The team also examined the present configuration of department locations and considered whether grouping departments differently or creating business groups would enhance our work process, perhaps eliminating waste of motion.

We had more meetings. It became clear that if we kept offices as they were in our building, we would not be able to meet our objective of staying within the existing building footprint. Since the first brainstorming meeting, it had been five long months of meetings, discussions, trial and error, and continuous frustration.

To be blunt, we were in the throes of a turf war that had raged from the very beginning. Those who wanted to keep their offices couldn't imagine working in any other way. Those in cubicles could not understand why someone could not work without an office. Tensions were high. Several members left the Lean Office team and others filled their vacancies.

To break the impasse, it became clear that the company's leadership would have to refine the objective. Looking back, it was another lesson in how important it is for management to articulate objectives very clearly and with no ambiguity.

One day our president put out a memo to all team members. A decision had been made. No one, including the president of the company, would have a private office.

The president was very frank in his memo about the dynamics of the decision:

> I believe that some additional direction is required to "unstick" the team and enable them to move forward with a clearer vision of expected outcomes. With that in mind, I have recently met with them and provided my version of our "workplace for the future," which is modeled after established marketplace leaders. Renovation will include the elimination of all private offices. As you read this, I can sense some of you see the "elimination of private offices" and cringe (especially if you currently are in an office). I am committed to an open, communicative, team-based office environment, and I look forward to an environment that allows us to further the collaboration and teamwork that I think is one of our greatest strengths.

OFFICE REMODEL BEFORE

As a result, the memo gave the team a clear, unambiguous direction on how to proceed. We learned a lesson in making sure we gave the team all the information it would need to move ahead and succeed.

CLEARING THE AIR

This very clear direction had the effect of clearing the air. The team reassembled and resumed work on the goal. Those who had been very adamant regarding their positions—including those who had been absolutely against eliminating offices—now began looking for ways to accomplish the stated objectives.

This was a very talented group, and it was amazing to see the emotional resources that had been consumed in the office/cubicle turf war now directed in a more positive way. The team developed the final layout of the office, incorporating ideas from across the group, and submitted the plans for final approval.

Since we would still be working in the building while the demolition and then reconstruction took place, the team decided on a four-phase remodeling schedule to reduce interruptions.

OFFICE REMODEL AFTER

There had been some debate about whether we really needed a large training room. Some team members suggested making it smaller, contending that more space could be used for office personnel. The team leader, though, was strongly committed to the objective established by the Lean Steering Committee: a training room large enough to accommodate 40 people.

The Steering Committee had reasoned that it should be able to accommodate project manager meetings, which often included other support personnel, ballooning attendance as high as 40. To make better use of the space, the Remodel Team designed it to be divided in half, allowing adequate space for both training and meeting purposes. Each half of the room was stocked with an overhead projector.

As we look back at this decision today and see the enormous amount of time our company uses that training room, whether for large meetings or divided into two smaller training rooms, we can rest assured that our decision not to compromise on the size of the training and meeting space was unquestionably the right one.

A Solution for Privacy

The team also creatively resolved the concern about how we would accommodate private discussions and confidential telephone calls. Eight of the old existing offices toward the front of the building that were not part of the demolition were converted into conference rooms/quiet rooms; anyone requiring privacy could use them when they needed to conduct confidential business.

The team also anticipated the question of how workers, especially those who had been accustomed to the shelter of a private office, would be able to concentrate in the new, open environment. Six months before the new space was to be occupied, the team created a special subcommittee that began sending memorandums to all team members explaining the etiquette our new environment would require. This gave all of us time to understand how we would have to change our behavior so as to function well together in this new way of doing business.

It was an especially important lesson for those who habitually tend to speak louder in telephone or face-to-face conversations. The subcommittee's memos expressed clearly, firmly, professionally—and repeatedly—the need for all of us individually to adjust, which helped to make the transition a lot smoother.

Benefits from Change

The changes in our office environment, although challenging, have produced good results. Now, as new people are hired into the organization, it is much easier to locate them in the office. We've eliminated the recurrent struggle over whether or not this or that new team member should be in an office or how big an office would be necessary, since, for the most part, all of the individual work areas are the same. When more space is required, the quiet rooms are available for use on a temporary basis.

The team that was in many ways the biggest and most contentious, responsible for a project that was to date the most ambitious and controversial one we had ever taken on, proved itself to be an outstanding team, delivering superb results and demonstrating once again the value of this new approach we were taking.

As we look back and reflect on the many major concerns surrounding the elimination of the offices, one point our president made indeed came true: This new environment *did* "allow us to further the collaboration and teamwork that . . . is one of our greatest strengths."

As I travel around the country and speak about this particular project to various groups and companies interested in the Lean journey, I hear from countless numbers of people who insist their management would never conceive of trading their offices for this open concept. I can only say that, having been in the office environment for more than 20 years, I would never want to go back to the environment of an artificial barrier between those in offices and those in cubes.

It's certainly true that businesses throughout the world exist in both environments; ultimately you will have to judge whether or not the open office fits your particular company and culture. For us, it was just one more success story on our Lean journey.

Kanbans

One deceptively small but remarkably effective tool of Lean is called *kanban*. This Japanese word refers to an approach to managing supply inventories. We have incorporated *kanbans* throughout our company and have been amazed at how such a seemingly simple concept can do so much to help us reach our goal with Lean: achieving value by eliminating waste.

Kanban means "signal": in this case, a sign that something must be replenished. Take office supplies, for example. Despite the promise of futurists, we're still a long way from the paperless office. Just check your copy paper invoices! Reports, letters, and all sorts of other hard copy documents remain a part of our daily business environment.

So if you're using copy paper, from time to time, it runs low. Then what? Someone is in charge of ordering more paper. That sounds simple enough. The person whose job it is calls the supplier and places an order using a purchase order requisition that includes the amount and type of paper and probably a number system to track supplies. Once the order is placed, the information is entered in the accounting system. Subsequently the paper is delivered.

The job of receiving it and properly stocking the designated storage space may fall to the person responsible for ordering the paper, or it might be delegated to another team member. In any case, the receiver and stocker gives the order's packing list to someone in accounting. Perhaps as long as a week later, an invoice for the order arrives; it goes to a designated team member, who enters the information into the accounting system. Often, but not always, there's a step for matching the packing list to the invoice.

At some point, depending on the accounting system, a check is issued to the supplier. And so it goes: a laborious process that's repeated many times for many different items, whether they're used in the office, the shop, or the field.

A SIMPLER APPROACH TO SUPPLIES

But now we're thinking Lean. So the next logical question is obvious: can we simplify this process? Or rather, can we simplify these many, many different processes?

Let's look at the very first step: someone is assigned to check that enough paper is on hand. But what is that process here? Does the person check on a scheduled date? Or could it work to have someone else let the buyer know when more paper is required? And that's where *kanbans*, or signals, come in.

Once again, we need to establish some baseline data. So let's study our paper usage: It turns out that we need a two- or three-day supply of paper on hand when we order, because that's how long it takes our supplier to replenish the stock after the order is placed. The answer is elegantly low-tech: we place a reminder card that says "Call Supplier Now" at the point in the stack of paper where we would have about three more days' worth of paper on hand.

Now *whoever* happens to come across that card while refilling the copier suddenly has a responsibility in the process: upon seeing the card—the signal, or *kanban*—he or she knows to take that to the person responsible for ordering the paper. That's what we mean by saying we want to get everyone involved and change our culture so that all feel responsible for making things organized.

Now that's just one step. We could stop there, and continue to rely on all the other steps for the rest of the process of ordering, receiving, stocking, paying for the order, and tracking it all in the accounting system. Already we've saved a little time; now we don't have to designate one team member who stops to check paper levels just to see if it's time to reorder yet.

FROM SHARING RESPONSIBILITY TO BUILDING TRUST

Perhaps you're objecting: "But then you have to rely on so many different people in the reordering process instead of making it one person's responsibility! That's not efficient!" On the contrary: passing on the responsibility to everyone allows for greater efficiency.

More important, though, it doesn't stop there. The process I've described offers many other opportunities for greater efficiency.

Remember that signal card? What if it isn't just a reminder note, but it carries on it as well all the specific information necessary to place a new order with the supplier? It could state the standard order size, the type of paper, the purchase order number, and the supplier's contact information. So the team member who comes across the card while refilling the copier takes it to the purchasing team member, who faxes the pre-printed form to the suppler along with a desired delivery date. Or these days, more likely, e-mail it, using a special template already created.

Whatever communications technology you use, you no longer have to write out another requisition since, through trial and error, you have determined how much paper you need for a specific time period.

So far, so good. But why stop there? How about helping the supplier work with us to create an even better process?

For that to work, our company and the supplier must trust each other completely. The sort of arrangement I'm describing typically commits us to an exclusive relationship with the supplier. Of course, that raises an obvious question: without being able to pit competitors against each other, how can we be sure we will get the lowest cost? The answer is we need to be confident of the supplier's honesty and integrity—and the supplier of ours.

Here's how it works. First, working with your supplier, you establish how often you need to replenish your paper supply and by how much paper. This may require some trial and error to establish both a reasonable quantity and a reasonable time frame for re-supplying. Then you make an agreement with your supplier to take charge of restocking on an agreed-upon schedule. As part of the agreement, you establish a fixed, reasonable price for a set period.

Now you no longer have to assign anyone in your office to check on the status of your paper supply. The supplier delivers as scheduled and drops off the invoice as well, complete with the quantity delivered. The company has one purchase order number for paper for the contracted time. Everything except the amount and time of delivery is in the system.

The result is likely to eliminate several steps in your organization, allowing you to more effectively deploy your personnel.

It should be obvious now why a partnership of this sort with your supplier requires strong mutual trust. This might not work for every organization or every supplier; you will have to decide what's best for you. But if you can partner with someone for whom you have high regard and trust, it is best to let the supplier handle the process.

KANBANS IN PRACTICE

Here's how we put *kanbans* to work throughout our company, in the shops, office, and field:

In the Tool Room: Remember the Tool Room event I talked about in Chapter Three? Many of the items that we stock are expendables or consumables—safety supplies, gloves, glasses, hand cleaner, and first aid kits, as well as items completely used up on the job, such as hole-saws, saw blades, and the like.

When we examined our process and established how long it took the Tool Room manager to review our stock inventory each week, we saw there had to be a better way. We had worked with one supplier for many years and built up a solid, trusting business relationship. We called the supplier and set up a meeting to discuss a better way of doing business. He had never heard of the term *kanban* but readily understood our desire to simplify the process of purchasing expendables.

We agreed to establish a minimum and maximum order size for various items. It would be his responsibility to visit the Tool Room regularly and resupply the bins. Since many salesmen already visit shops on a regular basis, this would not necessarily add additional time for his team members. We agreed to one blanket invoice each month for the items delivered, cutting down on paperwork. We also agreed to a fixed price on each item, effective for a year in most cases.

You may ask: how can you be sure the supplier is not billing for more than he delivered, since he is responsible for filling the bins? Once again, this points to the necessity of picking suppliers whom you can trust when negotiating such an arrangement.

As we considered whether to engage this particular supplier at this new level, we considered the long-standing relationship we had with the business and reasoned its leaders and team members wouldn't want to jeopardize it. We also began conducting occasional spot checks, a practice that continues to this date.

It's still a little unnerving to trust anyone 100 percent—but we're making progress and actually audit less frequently than we used to. So far, our trust hasn't been betrayed.

On the Jobsite: On almost any sizeable project, our people use a large number of hangers, straps, nuts, bolts, washers, all-thread rod, and similar kinds of hardware. Since we have three to four trades working on any given job, we decided to put together a team to examine how we could standardize the management of our supply of these items on the job.

Our standard practice had been to return unused items from the job to the shop in miscellaneous cardboard boxes. Then someone would have to sort through them, requiring a fair amount of labor. What if we could develop a better way?

The solution was hardware boxes. We selected an upright toolbox on wheels with built-in shelves, which we outfitted with bins of various sizes. All hardware is identified and stored in the bins. The wheels on the box allow easy moving around the jobsite. On larger projects, we might use several of these boxes to spare workers from having to walk long distances to retrieve needed hardware.

Once the boxes are shipped to the jobsite, we arrange for the supplier to come to the jobsite and replenish the supplies, just as we were doing in the Tool Room. Once again, the supplier would know minimum and maximum quantities to be stocked. We established prices for the hardware before the process started, basing them on standard quantities that we would order.

When the job is complete, the hardware box is returned to the shop in one unit, the items already sorted instead of jumbled into many cardboard boxes. We've eliminated all the time wasted sorting through

TOOL ROOM KANBANS

those boxes. And when the next job requires a large quantity of hardware, the hardware box is ready to be sent out to the jobsite.

In the Sheet Metal Shop: We fabricate most of the sheet metal components we use in our own shop. For some more common items, however, such as smaller-diameter round fittings, it is more economical to purchase from a shop that turns them out by the thousands.

We still maintain very small inventories, though. Once again we worked with a long-time supplier, explaining our desire to eliminate waste in our process. He was very accommodating and agreed to develop with us the sort of process that we had worked out with the Tool Room supplier.

We established minimum and maximum order sizes for items, then set up a routine for him to come to the shop and restock. We also established an expectation that he would make sure we did not run out of the items we require to fill an order for a particular job.

This particular requirement was a key component of our arrangement. Since we have many small jobs requiring immediate

JOBSITE KANBAN

attention, we expect to be able to send out all items required for that job at the same time to eliminate waste.

Some of these jobs take only a day or two to finish. In the Sheet Metal Department, most items must be prefabricated and not directly purchased from a supplier. With some components fabricated in the shop and others purchased from a supplier, it made the most sense to have the supplier deliver to the shop, rather than the jobsite, so that all components for the job could be delivered from one location: our Sheet Metal shop.

Given how short a time it takes to complete some of these jobs, however, it's critical for our supplier to be able to commit to delivering to us on time. Without that, we can risk cost overruns on such short projects—and the entire goal of *kanban*, cutting waste, will be defeated.

NO SINGLE SOLUTION

Now, you may have many reasons not to directly give a particular supplier the kind of authority over minimum or maximum order sizes, as suggested in these examples. In such instances, as we saw in the copy paper example, you can certainly establish some sort of *kanban*, or signal, that tells your personnel when it's time to order again.

The real bottom line is to continually look for ways you can eliminate steps or simplify the process. Studying your purchasing processes in depth will take some time; therefore, I suggest you start by looking at what in your organization seems to be the easiest to tackle and process.

Some cases may present an especially daunting challenge, but one that, if solved, would add greatly to your bottom line by eliminating waste. When that happens, as our own Lean journey has taught us repeatedly, you should go for it. And if you do, don't skimp on the time you need to really understand what the problem is. Too many times we are in such a hurry to solve the problem that we act without all the facts; then, before you know it, the same problem rears up again.

Our experience has taught us that often we spend more time on actually understanding the problem than in solving it. But if you spend that time on the long-range examination of the whole process, rather than the short-term part that's immediately visible, it will be time well spent.

If you look only at the short term, you're likely to have to revisit the same situation again later. You've settled for a Band-Aid as opposed to getting at the root cause. When you take the time to identify the root cause of a problem, you will find that even Lean tools that seem small, such as the *kanban*, can be an effective part of the solution.

TRUCK EVENTS

Looking for other areas in our operation that could benefit from Lean principles, we realized that our technicians' vehicles were a major source of waste. We decided to carry out a series of 5S Lean events, one for each of our service vehicles, in which we would work with the person assigned to the vehicle to reevaluate how it was organized and used.

Each individual truck—from the following trades: plumbing, sprinkler, HVAC, electrical, metals, and underground—had to be considered in light of the particular tools and materials it would be stocked with. This application would be different from previous ones, since it would involve just one person at a time—the team member assigned to the vehicle—as opposed to an entire department. However, we still felt that a team should be assembled to study the process and recommend changes.

STOCKING TRUCKS: THEN AND NOW

In the past, when we purchased a new vehicle, it was up to the individual technician assigned to it to transfer his tools and other materials from his existing van or pickup truck to the new vehicle and then organize it according to his own preferences.

That task could take anywhere from one to two days. Usually this meant putting things away just as they had been in the previous vehicle, without necessarily paying specific attention to any type of improvements.

In evaluating 5S events associated with the trucks and vans, it was very important, as with any other event, to find the right person with the right attitude to ensure a successful outcome and to devise a system that all could implement.

On our first Truck event, the team consisted of me, an Accounting Department team member, my assistant, a sheet-metal tradesman, the vehicle manager, and, of course, the technician assigned to the vehicle. Prior to the actual event, we met with all team members who would be getting new trucks that particular year to review what we were trying to accomplish with these 5S events.

The No. 1 goal was to make it possible for someone who was familiar with how the vehicles were organized and who needed an item that was kept on the vehicles to be able to find and retrieve that item within 30 seconds. This required a lot of visual cues, mainly in the form of easy-to-see labels, both on the bins in the truck and on the shelves where the bins were stored. A clear labeling system helped ensure that when bins or items were taken from the shelves, they were returned to the same place.

SORT

The first Truck event was with the Refrigeration Department, but we have used essentially the same process for our other department trucks ever since. A refrigeration technician carries a wide assortment of parts and pieces and various types of hoses. So the first step is the first of the 5Ss: **Sort**.

We completely empty the vehicle to be retired, placing all similar items on tables set up beside the vehicle. The individual technician is responsible for sorting through everything on the tables to determine which items he really needs. The other team members are there to ask him—repeatedly—why he feels he needs each item.

A word of caution here: team members need to approach this activity tactfully, and need to be clear that the technician understands all these questions aren't meant as an insult to his intelligence. They are merely a step to help pinpoint waste. The technician is the ultimate decision maker.

But as with every other event, there is a clear objective. For trucks, the primary goal is to make sure that they are under the gross weight allowed for the vehicle. For that reason, we weigh the trucks before and after the reorganizing project.

By reorganizing in this way, we have cut the weight of some vehicles by several hundred pounds; in one particular vehicle, we identified some 600 pounds of unneeded materials that we were able to get off the truck.

STRAIGHTEN, SWEEP, STANDARDIZE, AND SUSTAIN

Once everything is sorted, we can tackle the second S: **Straighten.** For the most part, everything on the shelves inside the vehicle is stored in plastic bins of various sizes. Once all the materials are in bins, the bins are placed on the shelves. But the bins and shelves are not labeled yet; first, we want to make sure that they have been properly organized for best utilization.

We also use the famed 80/20 rule—the so-called Pareto principle, named for Italian economist Vilfredo Pareto, who calculated in 1906 that 80 percent of the wealth was accumulated by 20 percent of the population.

For the vans, we identify which items are used 80 percent of the time, then locate them as close as possible to the rear or side doors or panels. That way we can eliminate wasted time and motion in getting things in and out of the vehicles by putting them within an arm's reach of the door, reducing the need for someone to walk inside the vehicle to retrieve the items needed most often.

Only after we have properly located all of the bins and hoses and assorted other pieces of equipment do we then affix labels to the shelves and bins.

Recall that the third S is **Sweep**. For us that can include a visual sweeping: we look over the van in its completed state to see if anything else is required.

The fourth S is **Schedule/Standardize**. With the first Truck event, we tried to set the standard to be used for a similar vehicle. To be sure, standardization could be challenging at times. Our company has roughly eight different trades, and each one handles two or three different kinds of jobs. Instead of always doing the same thing, our people are versatile and multi-skilled.

Initially that made standardization a problem. In fact, through our teamwork, we came to understand that not every truck for every different trade and kind of job could be set up in exactly the same way. Still, we could identify certain things common to all, and wherever possible, we made sure we were consistent—for instance, in choosing

HVAC TRUCK EVENT BEFORE

a standardized kind of clip to hang components in the van, or a common size and type of hose or extension cord.

At the same time, we always remain alert for a better way to organize our vehicles. More on that in a moment.

The fifth S is **Sustain**. Again we turn to an audit form, used to audit each vehicle that has been through this reorganizing process, to make sure we are sticking with what we set out to do.

Consistent Improvement

Once again we had achieved a success. From that first Truck event, we went on to many more, making this exercise a standard operational tool in our company. In the six years since we started reorganizing, we have seen constant improvement in the trucks, thanks to suggestions from the technicians and others who have been involved in these 5S Truck events.

For example, before the first Truck event, technicians at an initial meeting for the year strongly recommended installing drawers in the

HVAC Truck Event After

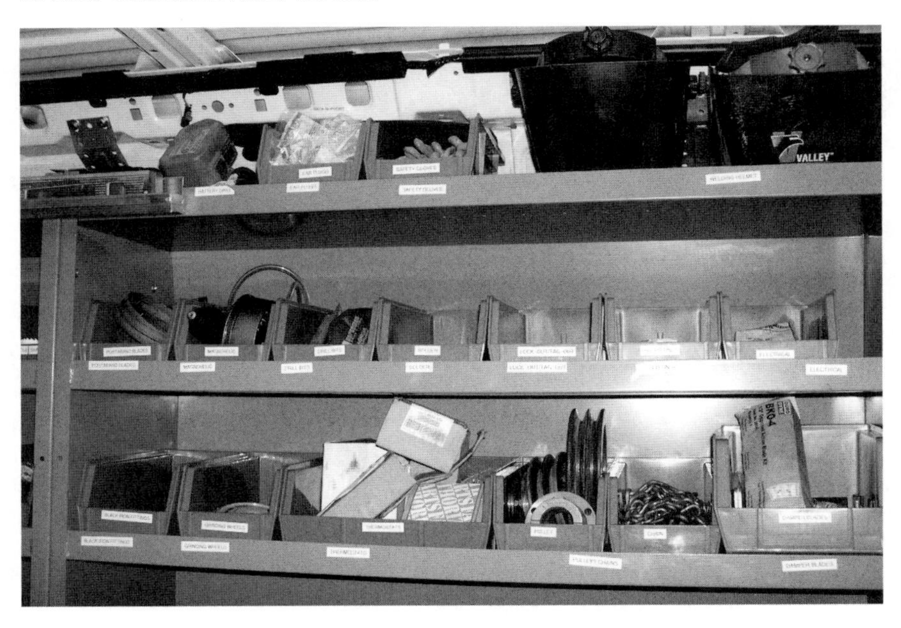

truck. The drawers were referred to as "rat packs" and weighed some 300 to 400 pounds. We accepted the technicians' judgment that the drawer units would improve the organization on the trucks.

But as time went on, we found that these "rat packs" lived up to their name: too often they were little more than trash receptacles. And as fuel costs rose, we realized they were weighing down our trucks and costing us money. We knew we would have to find an alternative, especially given the weight limits we face.

In addition to the rat packs, we noticed that any drawers in the vehicle also became prone to disorder. We needed a new solution to reduce these sources of waste.

AN UNEXPECTED SOLUTION

We were about halfway through the project of reorganizing the vehicles when both our electricians and our plumbers began using new carrying cases for tools and supplies. The cases were about the size of a briefcase and contained a number of different compartments that

SPRINKLER TRUCK EVENT BEFORE

could be removed individually.

A worker could carry an entire case or just an individual compartment to a work area and have all the necessary parts for a particular job. With some cases measuring four inches deep and others two inches, they proved to be very versatile, allowing us to store a variety of different parts and pieces in a very organized fashion.

Our Sheet Metal Department then devised a specific shelving arrangement that could accommodate all of the cases required for each particular vehicle. Depending on the specific use of the vehicle, some might have space for as many as seven or eight of these cases.

In keeping with our goal of enabling someone to find an item in 30 seconds, cases as well as individual compartments would be clearly labeled—for instance, "hardware" for a case or "3/8 drop-in anchors" for an individual compartment. This might seem like overkill: after all, most of the time the only individual using the vehicle would be the technician regularly assigned to it, and he could be expected to be able to find the item he needed without a lot of labels.

Sprinkler Truck Event After

In reality, though, we found that often a particular item had not been returned to its proper location and thus took longer to find. In addition, our technicians from time to time had others—especially apprentices—working with them and keeping their tools and materials in the vehicle as well.

IMPROVEMENT NEVER STOPS

In keeping with our culture and trying to keep open the lines of communication with our team members, as well as to enhance our apprentices' education, we meet with the apprentices every six months over the course of their five-year apprenticeship period. When we've asked them about our Lean process, a number of them have indicated how much easier it has become to find things when a technician asks for something from the vehicle.

But the most important benefit from our reorganized trucks is what they show our customers: that ours is a highly professional organization and that our people can do a much better job for them as a result.

We make many service calls, and we are hired strictly on a time and material basis. By eliminating the treasure hunt in our vehicles for something that might take as long as 10 or 15 minutes to find, we are adding value to our customers—and they know it.

Our experience in implementing Lean in such a variety of applications made it clear to us that there always will be continuous improvement with every process. We can never rest on our laurels: instead, our goal is to constantly examine our processes, always looking for new ways to provide greater value to our customers by eliminating waste. We must never become complacent with what we have accomplished.

The environment around us is always changing. So we must be vigilant not changing just for the sake of change, but to keep up with what is happening around us and to be sure we are providing the greatest value to our customers.

10

Daily Huddle - Project Schedule

The Daily Huddle-Project Schedule (DHPS) is yet another tool from the Lean toolbox. It is a particularly useful planning tool that focuses attention on the jobsite supervisor, the person immediately in charge of directing the workforce doing the actual work.

The DHPS has four components.

1. Measurement of past one-week schedule.
2. Six-week look-ahead schedule.
3. One-week look-ahead schedule.
4. Daily Huddle questions.

Since we were convinced that this approach was a useful tool, we decided to use it for our own benefit, whether other contractors on the projects did or not. You can imagine that it was more difficult to keep our commitments while others on the project did not buy into this approach. However, we felt very strongly we would concentrate on what we could control, and thereby eliminate wasteful use of our workforce and our resources.

During the weekly project meeting, the supervisor reviews what was accomplished in the preceding work week. He then asks each specific trade foreman what is planned for both the upcoming six-week and one-week schedules.

MEASURING THE PAST ONE-WEEK SCHEDULE

As is true with anything in Lean, you must be able to measure what you are doing if you are going to improve that process. Therefore, during the review of the past week's activities, the team strives to be sure that every trade has accomplished at least 80 percent of its promised objectives from the weekly job meeting.

In addition to identifying what they have accomplished, team members must also discuss the constraints that prevented their completion of any tasks and, if possible, identify specific, larger trends or external factors that may have contributed to delays. These might include another trade that was in the way of starting the work, materials that were not available, or information required to proceed that wasn't readily at hand. It is important to understand that on a typical construction site, many activities are proceeding simultaneously; to be able to accomplish 80 percent or more of what you plan to do requires careful thought in the planning process.

WEEKLY SCORECARD
(PREVIOUS WEEK'S ONE-WEEK LOOK-AHEAD SCHEDULE)

© GRUNAU COMPANY, INC.
Weekly Scorecard
Project: Hospital

					Constraint Analysis													
					Internal							External					Week of	4/12/2010
					Redo / Leave Out										Analysis (Type as "Y" or "N" so % calculates correctly in chart)			
Trade	Area	Repeat	Activity	Responsible Party	Engineering	Deliveries	Fab	Damaged	Missed	Lost	Not On Job	CO	Eng Delay	Other Trades	Y	N	73%	Reason for Variance
SF	1-B		Branches, VAV's, cond. Traps	John + 1									x			N		Waiting for final drawings
SF	1-B		B-Mechanical room	Bob +2											Y			
SF	1-C		Demo/rework VAV/baseboard H.W.loop then test	Tom + 2											Y			
PL	1-D		Domestic Water - finish overhead piping in bathrooms	Tim +1										x		N		Drywallers - congestion
SM	1-D		Duct Mains - VAV in water softener room then 12x12 duct to floor, cut tap in	Jane +3											Y			
SF	1-E		Dock U.H.'s, MRI FCU, misc.trim	Bill + 1											Y			
PL	1-F		Med Gas - overhead med gas mains - connect 1G to 1F, test, blowdown	Mary +1											Y			
SF	1-F		Humidifiers and steam filters	Ann + 1											Y			
PL	1-H		Waste & Vent - IUG prefab / install	Julio +2										x		N		Congestion
PL	1-H		Domestic Water - inwall prefab	John +3											Y			
PL	1-J		Finishes - set fixtures in available rooms	Johnny +2											Y			
PL	1-J		Med Gas - hook up, braze and test (5) med gas rails for patient rooms	Bobby +1											Y			

WEEKLY SCORECARD CHART

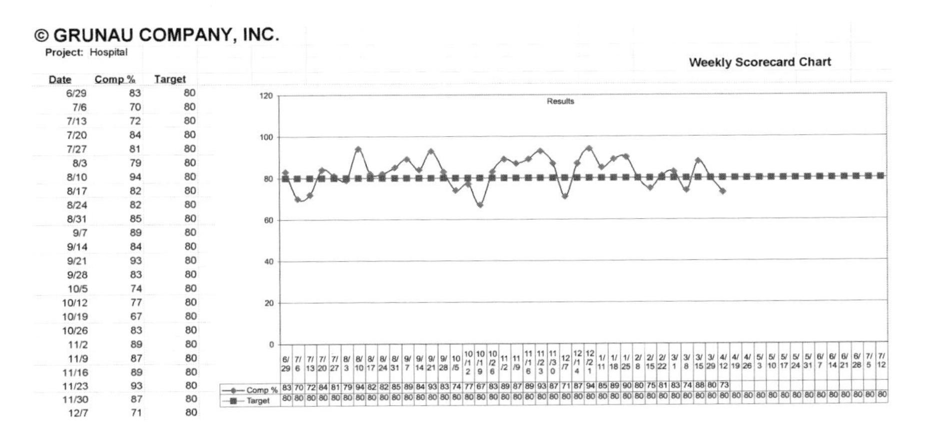
© GRUNAU COMPANY, INC.

Project: Hospital

Date	Comp %	Target
6/29	83	80
7/6	70	80
7/13	72	80
7/20	84	80
7/27	81	80
8/3	79	80
8/10	94	80
8/17	82	80
8/24	82	80
8/31	85	80
9/7	89	80
9/14	84	80
9/21	93	80
9/28	83	80
10/5	74	80
10/12	77	80
10/19	67	80
10/26	83	80
11/2	89	80
11/9	87	80
11/16	89	80
11/23	93	80
11/30	87	80
12/7	71	80

Throughout the project we would track our goal of 80 percent while trying to reach 100 percent. Some may ask, "Why isn't the goal 100 percent?" Since we did not control everything on a job, it would have been very discouraging to everyone involved to continually be reminded of not meeting the goal.

THE SIX-WEEK SCHEDULE

After our discussion about the previous week, we then talk about the next six weeks. As we look at the various upcoming tasks, we do not try to identify specifically who will be assigned any particular task, since construction projects are fluid. It would be a waste of time and effort to identify all individuals assigned to perform each task. Instead, using this schedule, we simply identify the project trade leader and the number of workers required when filling out the "responsible party" column.

On-time material delivery is essential to keeping building projects on schedule. The six-week look-ahead helps ensure that materials, especially those with long delivery lead times, are on track to arrive on the site by the time they will be needed.

But that's only part of the picture. Some material coming from

SIX-WEEK LOOK-AHEAD SCHEDULE

Six Week Schedule

Project: Hospital

Week of 4/19/2010

Trade	Area	Repeat	Activity	Responsible Party	Wk 1 4/19	Wk 2 4/26	Wk 3 5/3	Wk 4 5/10	Wk 5 5/17	Wk 6 5/24	Explanation of Constraints	Action Required By
PL	1-A		Domestic Water	Tim +2	x							
SF	1-B		Branches, VAV's, cond. traps	John +1	X	X						
SF	1-B		B-Mechanical room	Bob +2	X						fill-in	
SF	1-C		Complete bb roughs, test/fill	Julio +2	X							
SF	1-E		Dock U.H.'s, MRI FCU, misc.trim	Bill +1	X	X	X				fill-in work	
SF	1-F		Humidifiers and steam filters	Ann +1	X	X						
PL	1-H		Waste & Vent	BillyBob +2	X	X	X	X	X	X		
PL	1-H		Domestic Water	Tim +3	X	X	X	X	X	X		
SF	1-H		Area build-out	Greg +3	X	X	X	X			coord/drawings	
PL	1-J		Med Gas	Mary +1	X							
PL	1-J		Finishes	Tom +2	X							
PL	2-C		Finishes	Tom +1	X							
SM	2-D		Grilles and Diffusers	Bill +1	X	X						

around the country may take 12 to 20 weeks or even longer to be delivered. It is imperative to avoid surprises in the six-week schedule; if you didn't think about a particular long-lead-time item until the six-week look-ahead, it would be too late. So to really eliminate waste and make sure you are adhering to certain milestones on your project, you have to think beyond even the six-week look-ahead and recognize from the beginning any job items with long lead times that must be taken into account.

ONE-WEEK LOOK-AHEAD SCHEDULE

The one-week schedule is extremely critical in eliminating waste. One of the greatest benefits of a carefully developed one-week schedule is the reduction or even elimination of work stoppages. When work is assigned and workers are deployed on a particular activity, but then, for whatever reason, must unexpectedly stop and turn instead to another activity elsewhere on the project site, time is wasted. How much time? Based on our conversations with a number of individuals, from project managers to engineers to workers themselves, as much as one to two hours *for each individual worker* gets wasted.

ONE-WEEK LOOK-AHEAD SCHEDULE

© GRUNAU COMPANY, INC.
Weekly Schedule
Project: Hospital
Week of **4/19/2010**

Trade	Area (FLR-AREA)	Repeat	Activity	Responsible Party	Explanation of Constraints	M	T	W	R	F	Action Required By
SM	2-D		Grilles and Diffusers - install 20 grilles/day and finish installing 2 access doors in return ducts	Tim + Bob				X	X	X	
SM	2-DE		Flip VAV's D28 & E27	John, Julio, Bill		X					
SM	2-E		Grilles & Diffusers: install 20 grilles/day; finish installing 2 access doors in return ducts	Tim + Bob		X	X	X			
SM	3-F		Duct Mains - Cath Labs/Smoke Purge Duct - measure and send to shop	John, Julio, Bill		X					
SM	4-C		Grilles & Diffusers: install 20 grilles/day; finish installing 2 access doors in return ducts	Tim + Bob		X	X				
SM	4-F		Grilles and Diffusers - finish last 8	Tim + Bob				X			
SM	4-G		Grilles and Diffusers - install 18 grills & install 7 Anemostats in c-sections	Tim + Bob					X	X	
SM	4-H		Duct Mains - Finish last 4 pcs	John, Julio, Bill		X	X	X	X	X	
SF	ROOF		RTU-F piping - Pipe from floor to first coil	Ann, Bob, BillyBob		X	X	X	X	X	
SF	ROOF		RTU-B steam piping - Pipe from condensate trap to 4th floor	Ann, Bob, BillyBob		X	X	X	X	X	
SF	1-B		Branches, 7 VAV's, 7 cond. traps	Jane, Bobby			X	X	X	X	
PL	3-F		Med Gas: Cath lab outlets in N wall, demo existing piping in ceiling, repipe new in wall	Mary, Tom				X	X	X	
PL	3-F		Med Gas: Cath Labs - underfloor serving Cath Lab pedestals	Mary, Tom			X				

Why? There are a number of good reasons. Workers have to physically move from one location on the job to another. They may need to change tools and get different materials. Even the purely mental act of shifting their focus from one activity to something new takes time. Having to start and stop activities accounts for a large amount of waste—and that makes examining how and why it happens, and how to prevent it, integral to our mission in applying Lean to construction.

PUSHING RESPONSIBILITY TO THE FRONT LINES

How is this any different from other scheduling programs that have been in place for years? The answer is simple: in most jobsite meetings, the project manager or engineer might be responsible for speaking on behalf of the field crew and the objectives they expect to accomplish in the following week. Instead, the Daily Huddle-Project Schedule focuses its attention not on someone remote but on the person who works on the project every day. The project manager or engineer may still be present at these meetings, but the promise, the commitment, of what the workforce will do in the upcoming week comes directly from the individual on the job directing the workforce.

This approach calls on that individual to be aware that he is indeed making a promise, and that when it comes to anything under his control, he must stay committed to fulfilling that promise. Of course, there are times when circumstances beyond his control will affect whether he can keep that commitment.

Giving the foreman more responsibility in this way also requires people in that role to be honest. How many times have you seen an individual foreman casually promise that something will be done by a certain deadline just because he wants to avoid a confrontation in a meeting? Typically when that happens, the foreman doesn't really understand the rationale for the deadline—and doesn't really own the commitment he's just nodded and agreed to.

The DHPS is designed to foster openness and honesty on the part of the foreman as to what he will really commit to accomplishing during the following week. And that openness and honesty, in turn, go a long way in keeping peace and harmony on the job. Obviously we still encounter unexpected delays that inevitably leave some promises unkept. Even so, of all the systems that we have tried to track what we do and when we should do it, the DHPS is one of the best by far.

DAILY HUDDLE

The heart of the DHPS is the Daily Huddle, where we use a standard, pre-task planning card. This Daily Huddle Card is the size of a business card and is laminated. Here's how it works: the one-week schedule details activities planned for each day of the week. Then, every morning, leaders directing specific areas of the jobsite gather their team members and ask them the six questions on the card. The questions themselves took several months to develop, and they're very specific: four deal with goals for that day, the other two with safety issues for that day.

Question number one: "What are our productivity goals for today?"

DAILY HUDDLE (PRE-TASK PLAN) CARD

DAILY HUDDLE (Pre-Task Plan) 

- ➔ What are our Productivity Goals for Today?
- ➔ Do we have what we Need?
- ➔ Any Obstacles to Achieving our Goals?
- ➔ Does Anyone see a Better Way?
- ➔ Were there any Near Misses Yesterday?
- ➔ What Safety Hazards should we Be Aware of Today?

Lean Mission: To continually examine our processes to provide greater value to our customers without waste.

Remember, goals must be measurable: we are looking for a hard number on how many tasks would be accomplished that day. How many feet of pipe will be installed? How many pieces of duct work installed? How many fixtures set? Whatever is scheduled for that particular date, we want to know at the beginning of the day, specifically what the team believes it will accomplish by the end of the day.

Question number two: "Do we have what we need?"

Sometimes we'll start on a particular task and find that not all the material is there to complete it. This results in a work stoppage. I've already pointed out how much time can be lost, depending on how many people were assigned to that task. In most cases, it adds up to at least two to three hours of lost productivity. Asking if we have everything we need before we start should help prevent that kind of drain. It helps us make sure that we haven't missed something on the weekly schedule.

Question number three: "Are there any obstacles to achieving our goals?"

Okay, we've confirmed that we have all our materials—but is there some outside influence that might prevent us from completing this activity? Is another trade working in the area where we will be? Are materials stacked in the area where we plan to work? Will weather prevent us from achieving our goal?

Question number four: "Does anyone see a better way?"

We especially included this question for the benefit of all team members. We wanted to be sure that everyone, including younger members of the team, had an opportunity to express themselves without feeling intimidated by others. In training all of our supervisors on how to use the Daily Huddle Card, we emphasize the need to understand that some excellent ideas have come from those who may still be very new to their trade or profession. You know that old saying, "You can't see the forest for the trees." Sometimes the younger members of the team bring a fresh perspective *because* they're still so new to the work.

Question number five: "Were there any near misses yesterday?"

This question underscores, for workers, the importance of always being observant in their work environment and watching for safety problems that could affect them. The "near misses" they observed yesterday might not have been on their particular assignment, but could be issues that they will encounter today as they perform similar tasks.

Question number six: "What safety hazards should we be aware of today?"

Again the question is specific to that jobsite and to that particular day. For example, in colder climates, is there ice on the floors? In warmer climates, do we have sufficient means to prevent dehydration? Or, will there be specific operations such as moving equipment—loaders, trucks, cranes, etc.—that might present particular hazards on the job?

Questions five and six are last for a reason: we designed the Daily Huddle Card so that, when the meeting ends and workers go to their respective assignments, safety is at the top of their minds. How can they accomplish their assignments in the safest manner possible?

Finally, at the very bottom of the Daily Huddle Card is our Lean mission statement: "To continually examine our processes to provide greater value to our customers without waste."

To measure the use of the Daily Huddle pre-task planning card, on visits to jobsites I routinely ask members of the team what they specifically discussed that morning. I can learn by their answers how actively they're thinking about their work day. The answers I receive from workers who have performed the Daily Huddle are quite different from those who skip it.

Those who skip the huddle tend to be on autopilot, taking a vague view of what they will accomplish that day. Those who perform the Daily Huddle are demonstrably more focused on the day's activity, talking specifically about what their goals are for that day and what safety questions are foremost on their mind.

A Tool for Everyone

What I am about to say cannot be understated! This tool, the DHPS, can be effectively used by *all* contractors, regardless of whether they are using electronic scheduling or are still using handwritten schedules. I know this, because the basis of the schedules discussed in this chapter is the handwritten schedule prepared by the foreman of the six-week and one-week look-ahead schedules.

On larger projects, the DHPS uses an Excel spreadsheet to track its various components: the one-week look-ahead, what percentage of the previous week's activities was completed, and the six-week look-ahead schedule. But this spreadsheet is still based on the foreman's handwritten six-week and one-week look-ahead schedules. Using the handwritten schedule, the Excel spreadsheet is updated. On smaller projects, the Excel spreadsheet is eliminated, and we simply use the handwritten schedule the foreman prepared.

Even though all the foremen talk to one another regularly, it is extremely important to bring them all together for an hour or less to discuss all other activities, both long-term and short-term. This is so trades within the same company are less likely to interfere with each other.

In all candor, however, this has been somewhat of a struggle. Foremen who have been doing this work for years and years sometimes tend to resist putting in writing specifically what activities they are planning for one week and six weeks out. It's not unusual to hear them ask, "Why is this necessary, since I know what I'm going to do?"

And it's a legitimate question. Experience has taught us, though, that the more we write things down, the more things we recall to mind, the more we're able to reduce delays and the waste that goes along with them. We know our foremen are already writing things down and keeping track of what is required on the jobs. With this Lean tool, we're trying to give them a standard way to plan our jobs. We hope that, over time, we will become more proficient in our planning, eliminating delays, and achieving the ultimate goal of Lean: eliminating waste.

11 OTHER TOOLS

MANPOWER LOADING SCHEDULE

The single biggest source of uncertainty on a construction job is labor. Will we have enough people, with the right skills and equipment, at the right time and the right place, to get the job done on time and under budget? The answer to that question hangs on countless other variables: changes in the weather, in the schedule, or in the scope of the work; problems in coordinating people and materials; material not arriving on time; lack of information—those are just some of the potential stumbling blocks.

It seems logical to schedule the manpower before the job begins based on the available information and the overall job schedule. Even so, as you can see, that will be based on your best guess—and I do mean guess.

It is extremely important, especially on larger projects, to project your manpower based on the number of hours you estimate you'll need for the entire job. In essence, you're creating a curve of your manpower needs: a weekly projection of manpower. We call this our Manpower Loading Schedule, or MLS. We use MLS for all of our trades. Below is an example, focusing on plumbers.

Each week, we update the hours actually used the previous week, comparing that against the original budget. Although the pace of the job dictates the amount of manpower required on the job, it is necessary to make sure there are enough hours remaining to complete the job and still stay within our budget. We need to know how long we must have personnel on the job to make sure we meet the needs of the customer when it comes time to turn over the keys. This ongoing visual of the MLS serves as a measuring tool that shows all stakeholders in the project where we stand in relation to the overall manpower picture.

PLUMBER MLS

Manpower Loading

		PLUMBING (see notes below)							
		Projected			Calc'd	Actual			
Week #	Date (Monday)	# Men	CO#	# Hrs/Wk	# Men	# Men	# Hrs/Wk	$$/HR	Variance
1	04/29/12	28		1120	33.7	24	**1346.5**	$ 50.75	-226.5
2	05/06/12	28		1120	36.6	31	**1465.0**	$ 50.60	-345
3	05/13/12	28		1120	38.8	35	**1553.5**	$ 51.88	-433.5
4	05/20/12	28		1120	42.4	35	**1695.5**	$ 52.09	-575.5
5	05/27/12	30		1200	35.1	44	**1405.5**	$ 52.25	-205.5
6	06/03/12	30		1200	44.6	44	**1783.5**	$ 52.35	-583.5
7	06/10/12	30		1200	43.6	44	**1742.5**	$ 52.38	-542.5
8	06/17/12	30		1200	27.6	43	**1105.0**	$ 52.39	95
9	06/24/12	30		1200	39.7	39	**1586.0**	$ 52.23	-386
10	07/01/12	30		1200	32.2	39	**1288.5**	$ 52.20	-88.5

A FLEXIBLE DOCUMENT

As you can see from the above example, there is a fair amount of variation. Why? Is planning at fault? Not necessarily. Several factors can force contractors to make repeated adjustments to the plan.

As any project involves a number of companies, close coordination is essential. If for some reason a contractor fails to keep his promise to complete his work on time, the effects can snowball. Contracts typically include language requiring every contractor to do whatever is necessary to stay on schedule for completion—*regardless of the sequence of the work.* Therefore, even if one contractor encounters a delay, every subsequent contractor must adjust manpower to keep on schedule.

It is also not uncommon that customers, when they submit final plans for pricing, don't really understand their complete needs on the project. As the project progresses, new concerns become clear, adding to the scope of the work, which in turn adds to the manpower requirements. These changes may affect work already in progress, requiring all contractors involved in the change to react immediately.

By using the MLS to track manpower every week, we can identify problems early in the job. That enables us to implement countermeasures to keep the project within the budget.

GOOD-BYE TO THE PUNCH LIST?

It has been said that the last 5 percent of the job takes more than 10 percent of the labor to finish. There are a number of reasons for that maxim. One of the main ones is the inevitable series of punch lists—items at the end of the job that must be complete before the job can be turned over to the owner.

It's my dream that someday, thanks to everyone knowing and adhering to Lean principles in construction, punch lists will become a thing of the past. That will only be possible if every individual on the project understands that he or she must take the time to perform the job assigned 100 percent at the time of installation, instead of coming back to wrap up one or two items at the end of the job.

In the meantime, as we use MLS to plan our manpower, we need to ensure that we allot enough manpower toward the last 5 percent of the project that in reality accounts for more than 10 percent. In short, make sure you plan to have manpower on the job for the close-out, even though there is little actual construction work to perform.

A3: A PROBLEM-SOLVING SNAPSHOT

Another Lean tool is A3, a one page, 11-x-17 sheet of paper that presents a comprehensive snapshot of a problem: its background, current condition, goals to overcome the problem, root cause of the problem, countermeasures to overcome it and a plan to execute them, and the follow-up to make sure that the countermeasures were effective. The A3 can be used for other areas as well, such as status reports and proposals. We use A3 to solve problems.

There are seven elements to solving a problem. The A3 format standardizes those elements in a very visual way, so that everyone can see the problem and solution without a lot of verbiage. It's a welcome alternative to that old standby, the memo that goes on for too many pages outlining a problem and its solution. The A3 tool forces an individual to distill the problem to what is critical, leaving out unnecessary commentary.

This tool can be customized in whatever form fits your organization. You probably already have some process in place for solving problems. The advantage of A3 is that it helps everyone in the organization understand the problem, because every problem is presented in a similar manner. Selecting the key elements is up to you; by confining it to a single 11-x-17 page, you make the person or team presenting the problem and its solution work to follow the KIS principle: Keep It Simple.This allows others to see very quickly both the problem and its solution.

"WHY?"

A while back I was driving my mother to a weekend family gathering. At the age of 92, my mother is hard of hearing, and as we drove, conversation was frustrating at times because of her hearing loss.

Along the way we stopped at a resturant and I ordered two senior coffees, one for each of us. We sat at the table, I stretched my legs and decided to broach the question that had been nagging me.

"Mother, why don't you want to get a hearing aid?"

"Oh, it's too much of a bother," she said. "You and the rest of the family would have to take time from your busy schedules to drive me to all those appointments! I couldn't burden you with that."

"But that is really no problem," I sought to reassure her. "We're all here for you, we can make the time, and it's no imposition at all."

Silence. I asked again. "So why won't you get a hearing aid?"

"If I was more than 50 percent deaf in one ear, I would consider getting one," she said.

"Okay," I replied. "Let's assume you are 50 percent deaf in one ear. Why don't you want a hearing aid for that?"

"My friends say that all the hearing aids out there are ugly," she said.

I knew I had seen hearing aids that were, in fact, quite small and discreet. "What if I guaranteed you that we could find one that was almost invisible? Why wouldn't you want to get one?"

"It's too much bother—all those trips to the doctor to have it adjusted properly," she said. That again—only not just a bother for her family, but for her.

I still wasn't satisfied.

Perhaps my voice was beginning to show a bit of the tension I was feeling.

"If we were able to arrange without any imposition on family or yourself, why would you still not want a hearing aid?"

And then, at last, she told me:

"It is one more nail in my coffin."

This was the real, root cause behind her refusal to get a hearing aid. It would be one more sign that she was no longer able to live her life as she once had.

And it only took five "Whys" to get there.

SEVEN STEPS

1. Once you succinctly identify the problem, the first step in preparing an A3 is **describing the background** of the problem: how long has this been going on, and why is it important to solve at this time? This is not a one-page summary, just a few simple statements. What is the topic? What is the history of the issue? How does the situation relate to your business strategy?

2. Next, and one of the most important elements in the A3, is to state the **current conditions**. Take adequate time to understand the *real problem.*

In construction, we are accustomed to getting immediate solutions because we have real problems every day on the jobsite. But when it comes to constantly recurring problems, we tend to seek the solution before we know the *real problem.* That's why the A3 tool is structured so that much of the time solving the problem focuses not on the solution but on identifying current conditions that are affecting the present result.

If we fail to take this step and devote enough time to it, we are only partially solving the problem, and it will occur again. So let's start with the current conditions causing the problem. Do you know the real conditions? *How* do you know what the conditions are at the present? Did you personally observe what is taking place? Or are you relying on what someone else observed? To really get to the bottom of the current conditions, you must go to the *gemba*—the Japanese word for workplace: where it is happening.

3. Once you know the current conditions, you must establish your **goals** in solving the problem.

These goals must be **measurable**, not subjective. Don't set as your goal "to improve communication." Make it measurable. For instance, measure how many times an assignment is not completed as directed, even though you have given direction. Then set your goal to reduce the number of such instances by a target amount.

Ask yourself these questions: What is needed to minimize or close the distance between the current situation and the desired outcome? What is the desired goal? Be specific. How can you show where things stand today? Use visuals such as charts, graphs, drawings, maps, etc.

4. To establish the **real cause** or **root cause** of the current problem takes time and patience.

Too often we attack a problem by jumping to conclusions and implementing hastily conceived countermeasures. As a consequence, we fail to solve the real problem. Only after establishing the root cause, using tools like VSM, fishbone diagrams, or pareto (bar) charts, or asking the question "why" a number of times, can you develop effective countermeasures to overcome the problem. What is the problem; the *real problem*? Why does it need to be addressed now? Who owns the problem? This can be difficult.

5. Once you have established the root cause, you now move on to **countermeasures** to overcome the existing problem.

In most instances, there will be more than one possible solution or countermeasure. It is important to list all that seem practical. From an array of possible solutions, select the best one.

Questions to ask in this step are: What are some possible countermeasures? How will you choose which countermeasures to propose? How do the related costs compare with payback value? How will you get agreement among everyone concerned?

6. Next, establish a **plan** with the tasks required, dates, and responsible individuals to implement the solution. On the same schedule, you can indicate the progress in percentages and post it so everyone in the organization can see it visually.

Questions to assist in this step are: What is your implementation plan? What is the timetable? Who are the responsible parties? What other business resources are needed? Visuals are also helpful in this step.

7. Last but not least is the **follow-up**, to be sure you have indeed solved the problem. If it turns out you have not, start the process all over following the same format.

This step is sometimes forgotten because you are on to putting out

A3 NO-HUB PLUMBING COUPLING

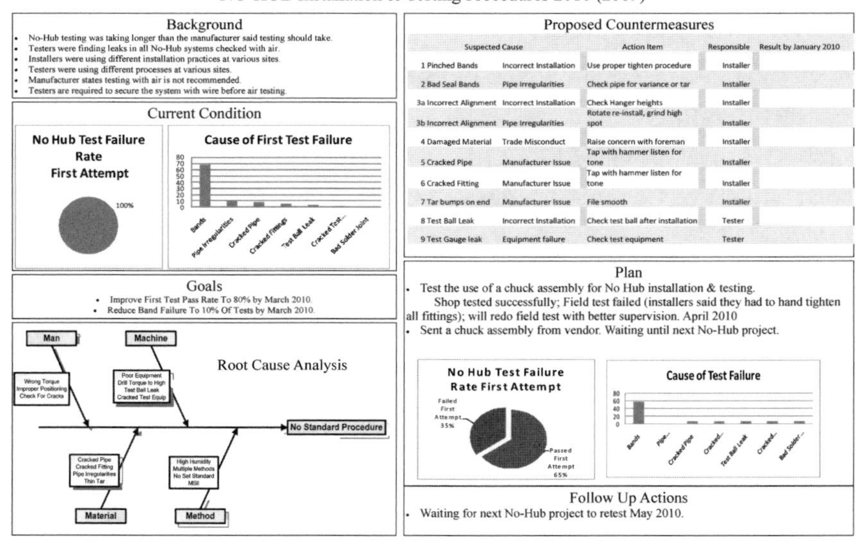

NO-HUB Installation & Testing Procedures 2010 (2009)

Background

- No-Hub testing was taking longer than the manufacturer said testing should take.
- Testers were finding leaks in all No-Hub systems checked with air.
- Installers were using different installation practices at various sites.
- Testers were using different processes at various sites.
- Manufacturer states testing with air is not recommended.
- Testers are required to secure the system with wire before air testing.

Current Condition

Goals

- Improve First Test Pass Rate To 80% by March 2010.
- Reduce Band Failure To 10% Of Tests by March 2010.

Root Cause Analysis

Proposed Countermeasures

Suspected Cause		Action Item	Responsible	Result by January 2010
1 Pinched Bands	Incorrect Installation	Use proper tighten procedure	Installer	
2 Bad Seal Bands	Pipe Irregularities	Check pipe for variance or tar	Installer	
3a Incorrect Alignment	Incorrect Installation	Check Hanger heights	Installer	
3b Incorrect Alignment	Pipe Irregularities	Rotate re-install, grind high spot	Installer	
4 Damaged Material	Trade Misconduct	Raise concern with foreman	Installer	
5 Cracked Pipe	Manufacturer Issue	Tap with hammer listen for tone	Installer	
6 Cracked Fitting	Manufacturer Issue	Tap with hammer listen for tone	Installer	
7 Tar bumps on end	Manufacturer Issue	File smooth	Installer	
8 Test Ball Leak	Incorrect Installation	Check test ball after installation	Tester	
9 Test Gauge leak	Equipment failure	Check test equipment	Tester	

Plan

- Test the use of a chuck assembly for No Hub installation & testing.
  Shop tested successfully; Field test failed (installers said they had to hand tighten all fittings); will redo field test with better supervision. April 2010
- Sent a chuck assembly from vendor. Waiting until next No-Hub project.

Follow Up Actions

- Waiting for next No-Hub project to retest May 2010.

other fires. Unfortunately, what occurs if this step is eliminated is that many times you fall back to what you have always done.

Questions to consider in this step: How will you know if your countermeasure works? What implementation issues can you anticipate? How will you ensure follow up and continuous improvement?

This has become a very important tool in creating a culture of active thinking: how to solve problems instead of just talking about how things have to change. This process takes a lot of time to get right. However, the more time spent on steps 1-4, the more successful you are at achieving permanent solutions.

NOT JUST TOOLS

Although all the tools discussed in the book are necessary to be successful in your Lean journey, here is the most important lesson: The Lean journey is not just about the tools, it is about changing the culture, the way team members think about their work each and every day. Many people whom I've shared Lean Construction with have told me that some individuals balk at adding Lean into their workload, as they have "lots of other things to do."

To that, I have a simple reminder—one we put on banners. The message is simple:

Lean is not an extra thing to do.

It's the way we conduct business every day.

12 The Bottom Line

If you've gotten this far, you're probably asking, "How is the Grunau Company different nine years later?"

Believe it or not, it is: very different.

Our emphasis on eliminating waste has cut our labor-cost-overruns on projects dramatically. By looking at our Value Stream on a typical project, we have streamlined our processes.

One example is the savings in material handling on projects. Working with our suppliers, we saved approximately 3 to 5 percent in labor. On certain projects, we may employ as many as four or more trades. All material is sent to the Grunau Company; in the past, it would take time to track down the foreman for the appropriate trade who was responsible for receiving it. The supplier, joining our quest to eliminate waste, applied stickers labeled and color-coded by trade (plumbers, for instance, or tinners) on all material sent to the jobsite. This very simple step saved us *more than $10,000 on one job alone*. We also arranged for the supplier to hold material until the trade released it just in time—eliminating the need to move the material a number of times before the actual installation.

Results from our vehicle Lean events show our production has increased by 5 to 6 percent—20-30 minutes each day—by eliminating treasure hunts. We saw a 13 percent MPG improvement in fuel costs savings from reducing weight on vehicles that were put through the 5S process—not to mention lower costs thanks to less frequent maintenance expenses, such as replacing brakes.

The savings don't stop there. Metal Shop hardware process changes saved us $30,000 a year. In one year alone, we saved $59,000 in our Tool Room by changing the process and taking ownership. We saved $45,000 in six months by having a vendor stock material on site. And since 2004, when we changed how we handled material in our Warehouse and in the field, we have saved $60,000 to $100,000 every year.

I hope you have gained some insight into what the beginning of the Lean journey in construction looks like. Much of what we've discussed is just common sense. But as I hope I have made clear, the Lean process involves everyone in the organization. It involves changing the way we view our workplace, whether we work in the office, the field, the shop, or a service environment. It's about allowing those on the front lines, in the trenches, to express their ideas with no fear of ridicule or intimidation. The Lean process enables us all to come together in teams and collaborate to arrive at the best solution regardless of individual egos.

To observe people in the company come out of their shell and perform beyond anyone's expectations testifies to the power of applying the Lean principles. I have truly enjoyed working directly with our teams, getting to know team members personally: their families, their likes and dislikes, their hopes and dreams. I have found that rewarding, but, more important, my viewpoint as a leader has been changed by the opportunity to work alongside individuals in our teams as a team member myself, not just the "executive vice president."

So where do we go from here? We continue to **sustain** and work to keep the momentum going. We cannot let the naysayers turn us away from the Lean process. As Paul Grunau said when we first started on our journey, "Who can argue with trying to get better?"

It is amazing what takes place over time once we immerse ourselves in the Lean process. It's easy to assume that once you have applied a specific Lean tool to a process, it's done. In fact, when you re-examine that process later, you're almost certain to identify additional waste. And the truth is, it never ends!

But that is a good thing. No matter what the market is doing, in good times or in bad, your team never becomes complacent. To be on top of the game, it is absolutely necessary to keep it fresh, to constantly challenge team members to look for better ways to improve processes, and to provide greater value to customers by eliminating waste. Being on top of the game requires vigilance on the part of leadership to provide the resources and additional investments to implement new ideas, and to consistently help new members understand the culture of always looking for new ways to do what we do.

Lean is NOT something else we have to do, it *IS* what we do. We have just started on this journey; we have so much more to learn. Toyota and other pioneers in this revolutionary way of doing business have been at it for more than 50 years. If they can continue their commitment to constant improvement, so can we.

Are the results worth the investment? Without hesitation, my answer is a resounding yes. It's true that I have been intimately involved in this journey as the champion of Lean operation in our business, so I can understand if you're skeptical: after all, am I really going to admit failure by giving any other answer? But I am firm in my conviction. And when I see others who have not been as involved in the process as I have been, especially our younger team members, begin to use the principles of Lean and change their approach to work for the better, it only reinforces my faith that what we are now experiencing has been well worth the investment we have made.

A FINAL WORD

I have been presenting the Lean Process of the Grunau Company around the country. Often I hear from members of my audience how much they appreciate the passion I bring to the presentation. Whenever I start one of my seminars, I even ask the audience to warn me if I am getting carried away in my exuberance, encouraging them to just gesture with their hands to lower my voice. And indeed, perhaps it seems that I do get a little too excited when I tell stories about the transformation of team members at the Grunau Company. But when you see the changes firsthand and can share that with others, it's difficult not to.

There is much more to our Journey and there are many other tools in the Lean toolbox that we have not discussed. For now, though, it's time to stop, reflect, and share with others what you have learned. I hope this book has encouraged you to investigate Lean Construction further. I was encouraged during the past decade by a number of individuals across the country, and I hope this book will encourage you to begin your Lean journey. I wish you success, and if you have any questions or concerns, I invite you to contact me at leanconstructionmaster@yahoo.com.

Appendix

Lean Journey Timetable:

October 2001: Attended seminar on 5S

Started 2003: Manpower Loading Schedule

March 2003: Memo to team members outlining Lean journey

Started March 2003: Assessment and training

April-October 2003: Tool Room event

November 2003-May 2005: Other events (Yard event/Metals event)

Started November 2003: *Kanbans*

Started April 2005: Truck events

Started February 2005: Value Stream Mapping

January 2005-November 2005: Service Department event

June 2006: Incorporated Daily Huddle - Project Schedule

Early 2006: October redefine objective—no private offices.

September 2007: Completion of remodeling 22, 000 square feet.

January 2008: Ongoing 5S events

Started 2009: Using A3

2009-Ongoing: Continuing Improvement

Index